best of
Missouri's Hands

Alternatives for the 80's Committee
a cooperative project of

University of Missouri
University Extension
Lincoln University

University Printing Services Columbia, Missouri 65211

Library of Congress Catalog Card Number: 86-71698
ISBN 0-9617089-0-5
MP 588

Manufactured in the United States of America
First Printing

Cover and Book design: **E. Rohne Rudder** and **Wessex Design**
Vignette photography: **Duane Dailey**
Additional photography: **George Laur** and **Frank Oberle, Jr.**
Vignette articles: **Linda Benedict**
Editing: **Karen Rohne**
Legal advisor: **Kenneth K. Wright**
Logo design: **Gary Hennigh**
Executive Editor: **Betty Feather**

*This book is dedicated to those artisans
who represent Missouri's best*

Alternatives for the 80's

Alternatives for the 80's, Executive Committee

Beatrice Litherland Smith, Chairperson, Dean, College of Home Economics, University of Missouri-Columbia

Marilyn Doerter, Dean, College of Professional Studies, Lincoln University

Roger Mitchell, Dean, College of Agriculture, University of Missouri-Columbia

George Nicholaus, Dean, College of Public and Community Service, University of Missouri-Columbia

John Oren, Associate Vice President for Academic Affairs-Extension and Director of Cooperative Extension, University of Missouri

Alternatives for the 80's, an interdisciplinary committee sponsored by the College of Agriculture, College of Home Economics, College of Public and Community Service and University Extension

Rex Campbell, Project Director, University of Missouri-Columbia

Project Leaders

Betty Feather, Home Based Business, University of Missouri-Columbia

Jerry Nelson, Agricultural Alternatives, University of Missouri-Columbia

Jeanne Nolan, Rural Entrepreneurship, University of Missouri-Columbia

David Sasseville, Horticultural Alternatives, Lincoln University

Jerry Wade, Referral Center and Clearinghouse, University of Missouri-Columbia

This catalogue was produced by the **Home Based Business Committee,** a subcommittee of Alternatives for the 80's

Betty Feather, Chairperson, Home Economics Extension, University of Missouri-Columbia

Edie Pigg, Project Assistant, University of Missouri- Columbia

Linda Benedict, Home Economics Journalism Extension, University of Missouri-Columbia

Wanda Eubank, Home Economics Extension, University of Missouri-Columbia

Thomas Henderson, Business and Industry Extension, University of Missouri

Bruce Maier, Missouri Ingenuity, Inc., University of Missouri-Columbia

Pamela S. Norum, Home Economics, University of Missouri-Columbia

Alma J. Owen, Home Economics Extension, Lincoln University

Mary Paulsell, Extension Information Specialist, University of Missouri-Columbia

Donald Schmidt, Marketing Extension, University of Missouri-Columbia

Robert O. Weagley, Home Economics Extension, University of Missouri-Columbia

Kenneth K. Wright, Law School Extension, University of Missouri-Columbia

Acknowledgements

Thanks to . . .

. . . **Extension Staff** throughout Missouri who promoted the concept of this marketing tool by identifying potential artisans, assisted them in the entry process and provided support to artisans as they expand their business.

. . . Vice President **Jay Barton,** Chancellor **Barbara Uehling** and Provost **Ronald Bunn** for providing seed monies to support this project.

. . . **John Oren,** Director of University Extension, who contributed financially to this book when support was critically needed.

. . . **Bruce Maier,** Director of Missouri Ingenuity, Inc., who served as a catalyst on the committee for proposing the catalogue concept.

. . . the jurors who helped select the artisans who appear in this book: **Dana Forrester, Pat Heller, Robert Leonard, Barbara Overby, Marjorie Prewitt, Cathy Smith** and **Helen Weaver.**

. . . **Deborah Rodhouse, Sue Andrews** and **Dorothy Stoerker,** secretaries who assisted daily by handling telephone messages, typing numerous drafts, and carrying packages and kept smiling through the entire endeavor.

. . . **Harold Perry, Ben Leach** and **Jenny Morrison** of University Printing Services who went the extra mile in the printing process to produce a quality publication.

. . . organizations, professionals and others who shared their expertise and contacts: **Columbia Art League, Kandys Bleil, Missouri Cultural Heritage Center, Kansas City Artist Coalition, Missouriana H.A.N.D.,** and **Craft Alliance.**

EXECUTIVE OFFICE
STATE OF MISSOURI
JEFFERSON CITY

JOHN ASHCROFT
GOVERNOR

May 22, 1986

WELCOME TO THE WONDERFUL WORLD OF MISSOURI CRAFTS

Missouri has a long tradition of producing some of the finest crafts in the United States. Missouri people have produced such fine craft items for centuries that many older items are highly sought by antique collectors.

This great tradition of high quality crafts has been handed down from one generation to the next, in some cases, and serves to inspire newcomers. The items in this first catalogue of Missouri crafts are entirely handmade by some of the best artisans in the state. I believe that the items listed in this catalogue are some of the finest to be found anywhere. Many will become tomorrow's heirlooms.

I thought you would like to know how to obtain some of these wonderful items. The University of Missouri, University Extension, Lincoln University, and the State of Missouri take great pride in sharing with you the names and addresses of some of Missouri's finest artisans.

Sincerely,

GOVERNOR

June 2, 1986

The work presented here in the "Best of Missouri's Hands" is among the finest craft arts to be found anywhere. It has been very difficult in the past for people throughout the United States to become acquainted with the hundreds of people who produce the fine quality and diversity of Missouri craft items. This catalog will serve as an introduction to some of our State's best art and best artisans.

The catalog is a product of an innovative program, Alternatives for the 80s, developed cooperatively by the University of Missouri, University Extension, and Lincoln University. The purposes of the several projects that make up this program are to improve the quality of life and the economic well-being of Missourians through new applied research and extension programs.

Cordially,

C. Peter Magrath
President

Ordering information

The items in this catalogue are either a representative sample of the artisan's work or the exact work that is for sale. Some artisans will accept commission work. If so, that is indicated. Some artisans have brochures available upon request.

Names, addresses and telephone numbers of artisans are provided so that the buyer can contact the artisan directly. Items listed in the catalogue show the retail price, which includes shipping and handling unless otherwise stated. Prices quoted are effective through June 1987.

Buyers planning to purchase wholesale need to negotiate directly with the artisan concerning price and quantity that can be supplied. The artisans are responsible for all contracts negotiated between themselves and buyers. Neither the University of Missouri nor Lincoln University is in any way responsible for contracts negotiated between artisans and buyers.

While every effort has been made to insure the accuracy of information in this catalogue, we cannot be responsible for errors in listing prices or other items.

Although not noted in the text, many items shown in this catalogue are subject to original copyright by the artisans and are reproduced here by permission. Consequently, no authorization to reproduce any of the illustrated works will be granted by the copyright holder of this catalogue unless permission has also been obtained from the artisan.

Table of Contents

best of Missouri's Hands

fiber art

"They take in the view and weave . . ."

Atop a bluff overlooking the Gasconade River and the lush, forested hills of central Missouri live a couple of weavers—Sherry and Jim Bingaman.

From the spacious living room of their modern home, an enlarged and remodeled cabin formerly occupied only by vacationers, they take in the tranquil view and weave.

They weave wall hangings—sleek, tailored tapestries. They use only pure wool, silk or wool-silk blends in a variety of colors to achieve the look they want. The design often repeated is that of a rolling landscape, not unlike the one from which they draw inspiration daily.

They sell most of their works directly to clients because they like to fit designs to specific interiors. A typical hanging is 3 to 6 feet wide by 3 to 6 feet long and costs around $600 to $700.

People find out about them primarily by word-of-mouth, since they only go to three or four shows a year. One year, when they were first getting started, they attended a record 14 shows. But that pace proved too hectic. Fortunately, their work is so much in demand, they don't have to do as much self-promotion.

They've lived in their idyllic setting near Vienna, a town of 500, six years, and have been weaving as their profession for nine years. Sherry, 36, an artist, had always been interested in weaving and had dabbled in it. But not until Jim, 39, an industrial engineer, decided to trade his occupation for that of weaver, did they do it as their sole livelihood.

Since they work and reside in the same place, their professional life is tightly woven into their family life. A typical day starts at 8 a.m. after Katie, their eight-year-old, goes off to school. They weave seven days a week taking turns caring for their one-and-a-half-year-old daughter Kory.

The interior of their comfortable home shows their well-integrated lifestyle. The two large looms blend into the living room with its expansive windows. The spools of yarn are grouped so they look more like accessories than supplies. For people who create wall hangings, their white walls are covered with various framed objects, ranging from artwork of Sherry's three artist brothers to yellowed newspaper clippings.

"I'm sure some people think it's easy to live our lifestyle—but it's stressful and chaotic like anybody else's," says Sherry, a cheerful and talkative woman. "Especially before a show," adds Jim.

But they don't plan to go back to their Chicago suburb, where they lived before embarking on their weaving career. "I used to go to work in the dark and come home in the dark," says Jim.

It has to be more pleasant to cope with a craftperson's stress in their setting—in a mild climate that still has four seasons, in a home that others would pay dearly just to spend a week in, and in a central location so they can travel more easily to shows and galleries all over the country—and with a view that's spectacular.

Sherry and Jim Bingaman, weavers

Shaded Landscape Tapestry
Woven primarily of silk and silk/wool yarns using various tapestry techniques. Peach/tan background with strong pastel accents.
Price: $725
Size: 38" x 62"

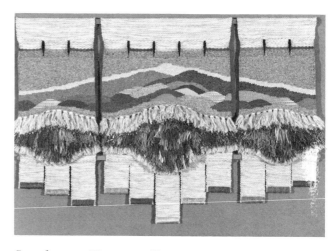

Landscape Tapestry A
Strong pastel colors woven using various tapestry techniques, with intricate shading and blending of yarns. Made of silk and silk/wool yarns.

Price: $1,100
Size: 57" x 41"

Landscape Tapestry B
Peach, lavender, and rose accents on a lavender/off-white background. Woven of silk and silk/wool yarns using a variety of tapestry techniques.

Price: $650
Size: 52" x 36"

Sherry and James Bingaman
Star Route 3, Box 14
Vienna, MO 65582
(314) 422-3004

Brochure available.
Commissions accepted.

Saddle Blanket/Rug

Woven in chevron pattern in your color preference or from handspun yarn from Missouri sheep.

Price/Size: 34" x 36"—$125
(available colors),
$250 (handspun)
34" x 70"—$250
(available colors),
$500 (handspun)

Wool Shawl/Scarf

Woven in overall lace weave from handspun wool of Missouri sheep or from prepared wool in cream, white, black, navy, or dusty blue (or will try to match color preference).

Price: $45 (available colors)
$60 (special orders)
$90 (handspun)
Size: 5½' x 16"

Linen Table Runner

In 100% bleached white or natural linen woven with lace border.

Price: $10/ft. in length
Width: 11-12"

Lisa Sell

Route 1, Box 90
Elkland, MO 65644
(417) 329-5559

Commissions accepted.

Old-Time Long Skirt and Sunbonnet

Wraparound skirt fits all sizes. Sunbonnet is from 100-year-old pattern. Both are machine-washable. Specify color preference.

Price: $40
Size: 44″ x 72″ (skirt)
Weight: 24 oz.

Cleo Dierks
Route 2, Box 185
Versailles, MO 65084
(314) 372-5190

Commissions accepted.

Lightfoot Rope Sandals

Handmade of 100% tough, durable polypropylene rope in a variety of colors. Lightweight, comfortable, machine-washable, and dryable. Rot-proof.

Price: $20
Sizes: XS (women's 5-5½)
      S (women's 6-7)
      M (women's 7½-8½, men's 7-8)
      L (women's 9-10, men's 8½-9½)
      XL (men's 10-11½)
      Jumbo (men's 12-13)
 Weight: 9 oz.

Robin Harris
Route 3, Box 90-A
Mansfield, MO 65704
(417) 741-6353

Commissions accepted.

Seminole Pieced Vest

Vests are made of a variety of cottons, glazed cottons, and rayons. They can be handwashed or dry-cleaned and can be made in any color combination. Sized to your specifications.

Price: $150
Weight: 1 lb.

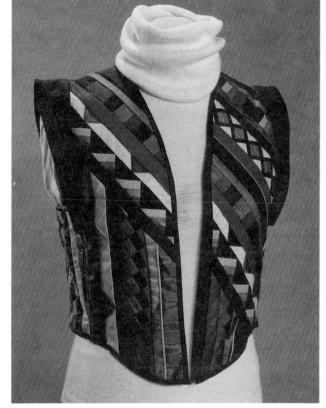

Jan Harrison
Route 1
Kingdom City, MO 65262
(314) 386-5150

Commissions accepted.

Amish Doll

This soft-sculpture doll has a black bonnet and lined pinafore with dress and pantaloons of matching Amish colors. Made of washable fabric. Specify dress color: maroon, blue, or green.

Price: $20
Size: 12" tall
Weight: 3 oz.

Cathedral Window Apron

Apron has handstitched cathedral windows on bib and pocket. Neck is velcro-fastened for ease of use, and the skirt is gathered onto a band with sashes for ties. Specify calico color: red, blue, brown, rust, or maroon.

Price: $39

Darlene Godsy
Route 2, Box 156
Mountain View, MO 65548
(417) 934-2637

Commissions accepted.

These batiks are produced with dyes and melted wax on cotton cloth. Colors are optional but must be within compatible groupings.

Grandpa Deckard, Rural Mail Carrier
Accurate enlargement of old family photograph. Size suitable for wall hanging or picture.
Price: $150
Size: 18" x 28"

Saint Louis Schoolgirl, 1908
An enlargement of a small, old family photograph. Suitable for wall hanging or picture.
Price: $120
Size: 18" x 22"

Resting by Still Water
Impressionistic picture of ducks.
Price: $300
Size: 40" x 52"

Carolyn Hendrix Hart
1420 S. Fairway
Springfield, MO 65804
(417) 881-6248

Commissions accepted.

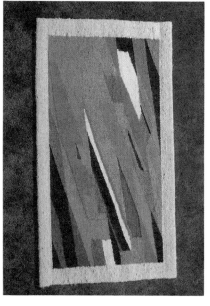

Birds Tapestry

This wallhanging is peppered with tiny, black clay birds sewn to the finished weaving. Woven with wool yarns on linen warp. The loosely spun yarns are hand-dyed, and the work is handwashable or dry-cleanable.

Size/Weight: 24″ x 33″; 500 gms.

Rainbows Tapestry

The diagonal design in bright colors is self-framed. Warp is cotton and weft is handspun and hand-dyed wool yarns. Handwashable or dry-cleanable.

Size/Weight: 18″ x 38″; 500 gms.

Morocco

Size/Weight: 72″ x 36″; 6 lbs.

Jan Landrum
11445 Conway Rd.
Westwood, MO 63131
(314) 432-8284

Commissions accepted. All work is $40/sq. ft. (excluding fringe)

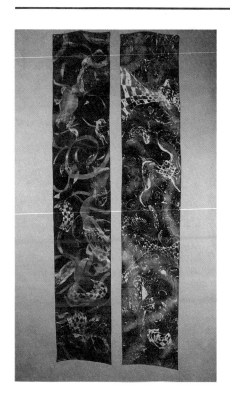

These handpainted silk scarfs have overlapping patterns that are wax and gutta resisted. Japanese brushes and French dyes are combined with water and alcohol, and the scarves are steam-fixed and handhemmed. Handwash or dry clean.

Batik Scarf A *(left)*

Price: $65
Size: 72″ x 15″
Weight: 2 oz.

Batik Scarf B *(right)*

Price: $70
Size: 72″ x 15″
Weight: 2 oz.

Anita Bleich
4227 Campbell
Kansas City, MO 64110
(816) 753-2726

Place Mats *(top)*
Handloomed in assorted colors and available in sets of 2, 4, 6, or 8. Machine washable of cotton or polyester. Specify material.
Price: $6 (each)
Size: 18″ x 12″
Weight: ½ lb.

Rag Rugs *(bottom)*
Handloomed rugs in assorted colors and weaves, with average size of 27″ x 54″. Machine washable of cotton or polyester. Specify material and size.
Price: $0.50/in. in length (excluding fringe)
Weight: 2 lbs./yd.

Bill Mobley
Box 233
Downing, MO 63536
(816) 379-2689

Brochure available.
Commissions accepted.

Rainbow Blanket *(left)*
Can be used as a baby blanket, couch throw, or, when folded, shawl. Made of 100% wool, hand-dyed and brushed on one side for softness. Woven in spectrum of colors.

Price: $79
Size: 48" x 48"
Weight: 1 lb., 6 oz.

Sunset Silk Shawl *(right)*
The colors of the sunset (from blue to orange) are reflected in the design weft. The fiber is natural and hand-dyed silk noil, woven in tabby and overshot technique. Can be used as shawl, table runner, winter scarf, or wall drape. Warm but lightweight. Handwash.

Price: $79
Size: 72" x 30"
Weight: 10 oz.

Hummingbird Country Pillow *(left)*
Woven in overshot technique, with cotton warp and wool weft. Filling is sealed polyester form that can be easily removed for handwashing. Specify color preference.

Price: $27
Size: 19" x 20" x 5"
Weight: 12 oz.

Patricia Brewer
Route 2
Unionville, MO 63565
(816) 947-3736

Commissions accepted.

Tunic
Knit from 2-ply cream Romney wool yarn with a front cable pattern. Made to be worn over hips. Comes in small-medium or medium-large.

Price: $175
Size: 27" x 18"
Weight: 24 oz.

Cable Sweater
Wishbone cable sweater from 2-ply grey yarn measuring 40 yds. to each ounce and knitting at a gauge of 3 stitches to 1" on 10 ½" needles. Sized S-M, M-L and one-size-fits-all.

Price: $175
Size: 23" x 18"
Weight: 19 oz.

All sweaters begin with Marjorie's sheep. She shears their fleece, combs the wool, and spins and knits the yarn. All sweaters can be handwashed.

Marjorie Cunningham
Route 5, Box 52
Columbia, MO 65

(314) 445-7596

Commissions dep
on sheep's health
weather condition

Amish Peacocks for Lee
Crib quilt of cotton and cotton blends. Peacock feather quilting is original; clam shells simulate eyes on feathers. Washable.

Price: $150
Size: 36" x 36"

Amish Diamond
All cotton quilt in traditional quilting designs. Washable.

Price: $100
Size: 24" x 24"

All quilts are machine-pieced and handquilted with 100% cotton batting. Specify color preferences. Quilts are signed.

Baskets of Amish Rainbows
Cotton chintz wall quilt. All materials are washable, but chintz will retain highest sheen with limited washings. Vacuuming recommended.

Price: $150
Size: 36" x 36"

(detail)

Linda Carlson
Route 3, Orchard Heights
Mexico, MO 65265
(314) 581-8643

Commissions accepted.

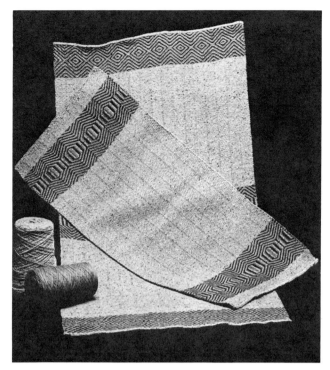

"Designs from the Loom" Saddle Blanket Rug

All wool and reversible rugs are of a twill weave developed by Mary Meigs Atwaler in 1920. Dry clean only. Also available as reversible summer and winter and hit and miss rugs of cotton.

Price/Size/Weight: $160 (54" x 26"; 3 lbs.)
$225 (60" x 36"; 4 ½ lbs.)

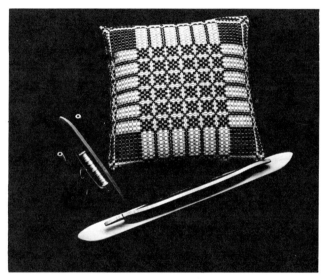

"Designs from the Loom" Place Mats

Place mats and matching runner of cotton and polyester blend. Machine-washable, dry flat or over hangers. Specify color preference. Available in sets of 4, 6, or 8.

Price: $27.50 (set of 4 plus runner)
Size: 20" x 14"
Weight: 1 lb., 8 oz.

Pillow in Overshot Pattern

Woven in wool with natural cotton warp, the pillow shown is a copy of a coverlet woven in 1860 (other patterns available). Handwash with care.

Price: $50 ($60 with pattern on both sides)
Size: 18" x 18" x 3"
Weight: 1½ lb.

Marge Wallis
Route 1, Box 175
Willard, MO 65781
(417) 742-2577

Commissions accepted.

(detail)   *(detail)*

Jeune Fille (Little Girl)
Handwoven tapestry based on slide taken at
Tuileries Park in Paris. Weaving similar to the
labor-intensive French Gobelin tapestry
technique.

Price: $1,600
Size: 40" x 36"
Weight: 2 lbs., 9 oz.

Le Jeu (The Game) *(opposite page)*
This triptych is of cotton, wool, and cowhair
handwoven at seven threads per inch. It is
based on a slide of four elderly men playing
boccie ball at the Tuileries Park in Paris.

Price: $3,664
Size: 50" x 63¾" (total triptych)
Weight: 6 lbs., 5 oz.

Deann Joy Rubin
1284 Beaver Creek Rd.
Chesterfield, MO 63017
(314) 532-4932

Commission work only
(price: $170-$200 per sq. ft.)

Handwoven Shawl

Made of acrylic/cotton yarn with lace border and 2" fringe. Machine wash, tumble or line dry.

Price: $40
Size: 66" x 24"
Weight: 9 oz.

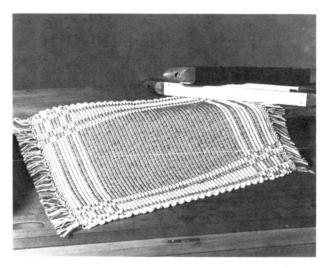

Guest Towels

Handwoven of durable cotton and finished with short fringe, these towels can be machine washed, tumbled dry. Specify color: blue/white stripe, white/blue stripe, pink/white stripe, white/pink stripe.

Price: $10 (set of 2)
Size: 15" x 11"
Weight: 3 oz. (per set)

Log Cabin Place Mats

Handwoven, reversible cotton place mats. Handwash and line dry. Specify color: blue/white or brown/natural.

Price: $25 (set of 4)
Size: 18" x 12"
Weight: 20 oz. (per set)

Jean Whitworth
Box 13
Moundville, MO 64771
(417) 922-3459

Commissions accepted.

Colonial Coverlet

Colonial reproductions handwoven in many patterns using cotton or linen woven with wool (pictured is "Federal Knot"). Woven for single, double, queen, or king sized beds in choice of color. Specify material, size, and color. Inquire for prices for other sizes.

Price: $550 (double)
Size: 95" x 80"

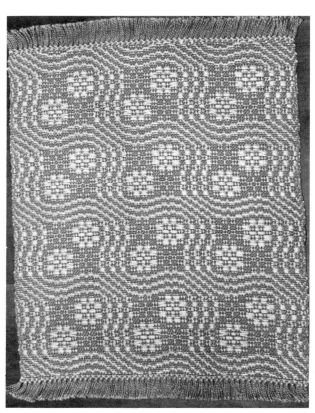

Place Mat

Handwoven from pearl cotton in "Cat's Tracks and Snail's Trails" pattern. Available in any desired size, material, or pattern. Matching runners available. Inquire for prices of other materials.

Price: $12.50 (pearl cotton)
Size: 18" x 13"

Shawl

Handwoven of 100% wool in plain weave using textured yarn, or in cotton or blended yarn. Can be made with pattern at each end or throughout. Specify color, fabric, pattern.

Price: $160
Size: 72" x 25"

J. Taylor Smith
Keelor Handwovens
P.O. Box 8
Arrow Rock, MO 65320
(816) 837-3328

Brochure available.
Commissions accepted.

Pheasant Family Quilt

Made in a combination of hand applique, patchwork, and embroidery, with textile paints for grass. Fabric is washable, color-fast cotton and cotton blends with polyester batting. Natural colors only, on off-white background and back. Handquilted. Every quilt custom-made in any size from 45" to 120".

Price: $7/sq. ft.
Weight: 6 lbs.

Dove of Peace Quilt

An original combination of patterns in washable calicos, with dacron batting and plain matching back. Every visible stitch by hand. No two quilts alike except if matched pair. Specify size from 36" to 120" (but not condensed work). Available in blue, brown, or burgundy with any accent color. Can be signed and dated.

Price: $7/sq. ft.
Weight: 6 lbs.

Louise Martin
Route 3, Box 253
Memphis, MO 63555
(816) 883-5560

Brochure forthcoming.
Commissions accepted.

Warp Equals Weft

This handwoven shawl is a plaid or plain triangle constructed on a frame loom of "found" materials and woven with the warp threads becoming the weft. Specify material, plaid or plain, and color preference.

Price: $60 (mohair/wool/
      acrylic), $50 (acrylic or
      acrylic/nylon)
Size: 73" x 50" x 50" (plus fringe)
Weight: 10 oz.

Canvas Weave Baby Blanket

Blanket is available in wool, cotton, or acrylic. Model shown is a canvas weave pattern, but other designs are available. Specify material and color: white or pastel with white background.

Price: $45 (all cotton or wool),
$30 (acrylic)
Size: 49" x 40"
Weight: 26 oz.

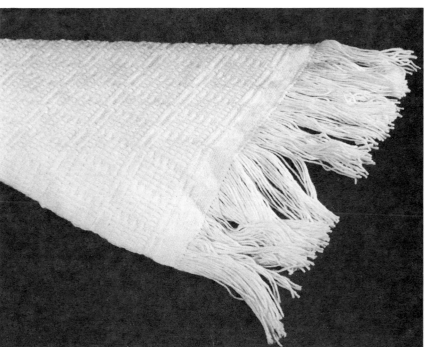

Sue Crews
P.O. Box 1630
Rolla, MO 65401
(314) 341-3873

Commissions accepted.

Hand-Loomed Bags
Available in cotton or polyester in any color
combination and lined with "home-spun"
material with inside pockets.
Machine-washable.

Price: $20
Size: 13" x 13"

Reta V. Myers
Oxford Originals
Route 1, Box 57
Parnell, MO 64475
(816) 986-3355

Angora Sweater
This sweater is 50% wool and 50% angora,
blended before spinning. Natural colors.
Handwashable.

Price: $175
Size: S, M, L

David Gentzsch
Box 69
Jamestown, MO 65046
(816) 849-2391

Brochure available.
Commissions accepted.

Delectable Mountain Quilt
Patterned from a quilt on display in the Jay
Historical Society, Farmington, Maine, this
quilt is pieced from white and green print
cotton/dacron fabric. Dacron filler and
cotton/dacron lining. Machine quilted with
handguided decorative design. Washable.

Price: $607.50
Size: 87" x 92"
Weight: 4 lbs.

Madge Finley
Route 1, Box 145
Holcomb, MO 63852
(314) 792-3623

Commissions accepted.

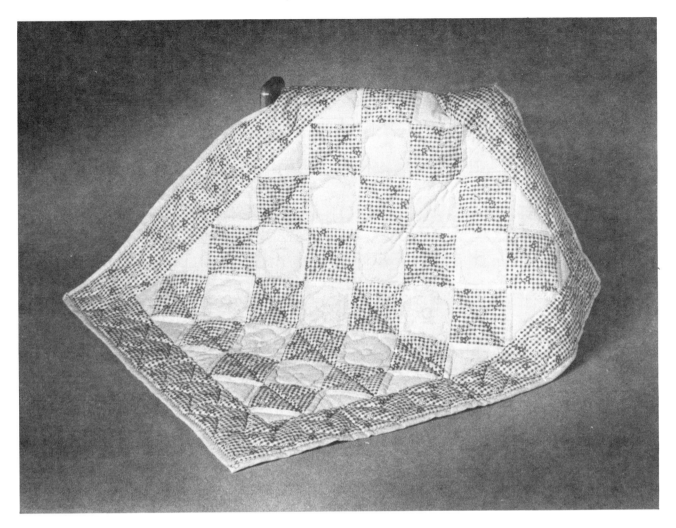

Field of Flowers Quilt
Miniature quilt or wall-hanging is handstitched
with cotton calico prints and solids. Available
in country red/white, indigo blue/white, forest
green/white, and warm browns/ecru.
Handwashable.

Price: $48
Size: 22″ x 26″
Weight: 6 oz.

Raeann Lenzini
611 Sunset
Macon, MO 63552
(816) 385-4719

Brochure available.
Commissions accepted.

Designer Yarns

Handspun natural fibers in natural or hand-dyed vegetable colors, all colorfast and fade-resistant. Fibers include wools, mohair, silk, angora, alpaca, cotton, linen, and fiber blends. Yarns are designed with solid, variegated, frosted, or blended colors. Available in single-, 2-, or 3-plies. Prices start at $3.50/oz. Send $2 for sample card (reimbursed with first order).

One-of-a-Kind Designer Pillows

Handspun, handwoven 100% genuine Navajo Churro wool. Natural colors of black, silver, white, brown, and tan.

Price: $135 (100% polyester fiberfill with separate lining)
$145 (natural down fill with ticking lining)
$150 (with opossum or muskrat tanned-by-hand fur strips)
$160 (fur and natural down fill)
Size: 14" x 16" (approx.)

One-of-a-Kind Triangular Shawls

Handspun, handwoven 100% lustrous Romney wool or 60%/40% blend 2- ply Romney/mohair with colors vegetable-dyed by hand. Full spectrum of colors available; colorfast and fade resistant. Also 100% genuine Navajo Churro wool in natural colors. Other materials available.

Price: Romney or Churro—$137,
Romney/Mohair—$182
Size: 6' x 3'

Carol Leigh Brack-Kaiser
Route 12, Box 349
Columbia, MO 65201
(314) 874-2233

Brochure available.
Commissions accepted.

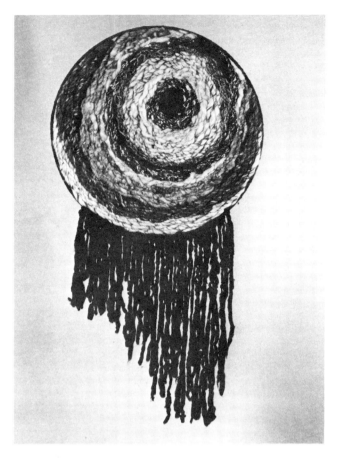

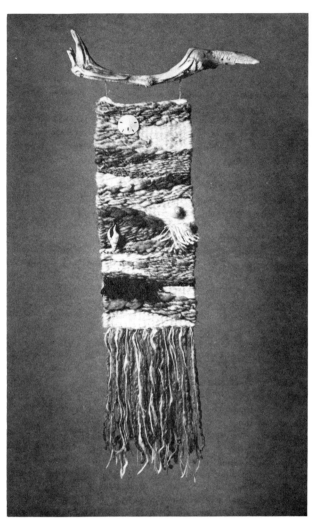

Wall Hangings

Made from handspun wool and mohair from artist's sheep and angora goats. Natural colors. Variety of sizes, shapes, and prices available.

Price: $65 (large brown round)
$60 (grey sea shell)
Size: 21" (round), 37" x 10" (sea shell)

Paulette Moore
Route E, Box 631
Caulfield, MO 65626
(417) 284-3252

Commissions accepted.

Handwoven Scarf

Warm, soft scarf of handspun, Missouri-grown mohair and wool in their natural off-white color. Available as shown or in larger, wraparound length.

Price: $35
Size: 45" x 10"
Weight: 8 oz.

Barbara Zernicke
Route 3, Box 139R
St. James, MO 65559
(314) 699-4288

Handwoven Rectangular Shawl
Two-textured, natural-colored, 100% cotton
yarns are used to form this shawl. Yarn is
commercially prepared. Can be handwashed or
dry-cleaned.

Price: $90
Size: 60" x 60" (18" fringe)

R. Gordon Tompkins
Warped Thoughts
821 E. Lexington
Independence, MO 64050
(816) 836-5645
(816) 252-8855

Commissions accepted.

These handmade Christmas trees have branches that project outward, adding breadth without using floorspace. The embroidered felt trees even accept your own ornaments. They are simple to hang with a rod or tacks and are easily stored in their own bags.

Tradition *(opposite page, top)*
Gold accents, satin lights, and bright fabric packages on red quilted background.
Price: $620
Size: 65" x 42" x 6"
Weight: 4 lbs.

Victorian *(opposite page, bottom)*
Pink nosegays, white satin candles, and appliqued packages on a cranberry quilt.
Price: $650
Size: 66" x 42" x 6"
Weight: 4 lbs.

Tartan *(this page)*
Bright red apples, plaid bows, and tartan-wrapped gifts below, appliqued to a cheery quilted background.
Price: $620
Size: 64" x 41" x 6"
Weight: 4 lbs.

Nannette N. Anthony
835 Green Lantern
Ballwin, MO 63011
(314) 391-9312

Commissions accepted.

Each silk scarf is stretched over a frame, handpainted, steamed to set the dyes, and drycleaned. They can be handwashed or drycleaned.

Scarf C
Sunlight streaming through a thick forest is the subject of this scarf.

Price: $80
Size: 60" x 15"

Scarf A
The mountains of New Mexico were the inspiration for this scarf, conveying the subtle gradations in color and distance.

Price: $60
Size: 60" x 15"

Scarf B
This scarf represents pebbles on a beach.

Price: $60
Size: 36" x 36"

Valerie Doran
7541 Wyoming
Kansas City, MO 64114
(816) 333-8718

Commissions accepted.

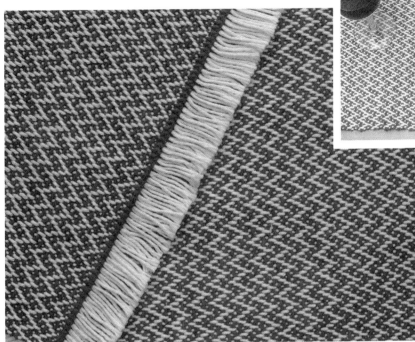

Twill Place Mat
Handwoven of 100% cotton and hemstitched by hand. Handwash in cold water and dry flat.

Price: $8
Size: 12¾" x 18"
Weight: 3 oz.

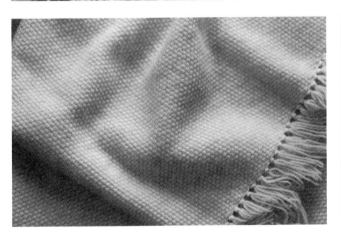

Baby Blanket
Handwoven in basketweave pattern of 96% acrylic for softness and 4% wool for warmth. Machine wash and tumble dry. Choose pastel yellow or pink.

Price: $25
Size: 29" x 34"
Weight: 8 oz.

Cotton Towel
Handwoven dishtowel, 100% cotton. Machine wash warm, and tumble dry.

Price: $12
Size: 16¾" x 27"
Weight: 3½ oz.

Dawn V. Yancey
The Sunrise Collection of Handwovens
Route 3, Box 35A
Fulton, MO 65251
(314) 642-7207

Commissions accepted.

Caped Frock Coat

This design is an Indian adaptation of a European design, using native materials. The elkskin coat could have been worn as early as the French and Indian War and was worn through the 1860s. Other items shown are leather pants, shirt, plain belt, beaded belt, hat, leggings, moccasins, pipe bag, choker necklace, and neck knife.

Price: $1,880 (complete outfit)

Woman's Dress, Blackfoot Style

Based on several paintings by Karl Bodmer in 1833 as he traveled along the Missouri River, this elkskin dress is decorated with glass beadwork of the type done by the Blackfoot women..Other items shown are moccasins, belt, belt pouch, beaded belt set, and hat.

Price: $1,375 (complete outfit)

Leather Indian Dolls

Made with deerskin and sewn by hand, these dolls are based on originals made 100 to 200 years ago by different Indian tribes. Hair is horsehair, the clothes are cotton and leather.

Price: $175 (all handsewn), $95 (partially
            machine-sewn)
Size: 12" tall
Weight: 1 lb.

Karalee K. Tearney
201 Morgan St.
P.O. Box 127
Arrow Rock, MO 65320
(816) 837-3261

Brochure available.
Commissions accepted.

Ultrasuede Shoulder Bag
Combination of ultrasuede and snakeskin,
designed in a square zippered pouch with·a
shoulder strap. Available in red with navy
trim, black with black trim, and black with
grey trim.

Price: $39
Size: 7″ x 8″ x 1″ (strap: 35″)
Weight: 6 oz.

Jeannette Fischer
P.O. Box 14
Lohman, MO 65053
(314) 782-4594

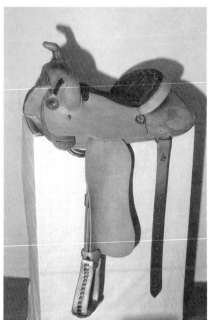

Handmade Boots
Designed and fitted to the individual and available in top grain calf, bullhide, shark, elephant, or other exotics.

Price: $225 (and up)

Custom Saddles
Handcrafted and fitted for both horse and rider comfort and needs.

Price: $850 (and up)
Size: 36" x 18" x 24"
Weight: 30-40 lbs.

Ken Bledsoe
Ken's Kustom Leather
R.R. 3
St. Joseph, MO 64505
(816) 324-4906

Brochure available.
Commissions accepted.

Leather Coat
Durable coat with two hand pockets in front and one snap closure pocket inside. Leather covered elastic waistband, heavy-duty brass zipper, bi-swing action back, underarm gussets, and nylon stitching. Specify black, brown, rust, or tan.

Price: $250 (longs: 10% extra, sizes 45-50: 10% extra)
Sizes: 36-50 regular and long

Leather Travel Bag
Bag has four zippered compartments, brass zippers, one outside pocket, 1¼" x 40" strap, and nylon stitching. Completely repairable.

Price: $139
Size: 10" x 10" x 14"

Leather Bag
Bag has two zippered compartments and one outside pocket, brass zippers, 1¼" x 40" strap, and nylon stitching. Completely repairable.

Price: $69
Size: 7½" x 3¾" x 11"

David M. Oswald
Route 7, Box 145
Columbia, MO 65202
(314) 442-7306

Commissions accepted.

metal

"He preserves the past with his blacksmithing . . ."

With hammer and anvil, Darold Rinedollar, blacksmith, creates more with metal than gates and candle holders. He preserves the past using techniques handed down from master to apprentice since the 1500's.

His ornate gates and curved candlesticks, featured in the "Best of Missouri's Hands" catalogue, are two of the many products he makes at his blacksmithing shop in Augusta.

Blacksmithing is one of those crafts impossible to learn well except from somebody else. Darold, 46, was an apprentice for two years under two old German blacksmiths. That was back in New York 26 years ago. Now Darold has apprentices, too.

You have to be there sweating alongside a seasoned professional to distinguish the hundreds of shades of red, orange, yellow and white that iron goes through as it's heated and cooled with precise blasts from the bellows. . . . You have to witness which exact color allows you to beat the iron to a sharp point, bend a curve or weld two strips together. . . . You have to hear the reasons for techniques that have survived centuries. . . .

These sensory experiences are often lost as modern people take up old trades. But not in Darold's case.

As he restored a wrought iron gate, he carefully hammered a six-inch piece until it was 23 inches long to get out the impurities and add strength, as was done in the old days. "Nowadays some people would just take a long piece and be done with it," he laments.

As you drive into Augusta, you don't have to ask which way to Darold's blacksmith shop. You can hear the dink-dink-dink of metal hitting metal.

As you enter the dark, antiquated, concrete-block shop, you're taken back through time as smells of hot iron and burning coal and the sight of tools cluttering every corner fill your senses, just as they must have your ancestors'.

Darold bought the place 10 years ago. It had originally been a blacksmith shop converted to a car garage—the fate of many such establishments. It's next to the feedmill so farmers could conveniently get wagons fixed and horses shod while in town to buy and sell supplies.

Darold still does a little shoeing in those rare cases when ready-made horseshoes don't fit problem hooves. But most of his income comes from the gates. He works closely with customers to come up with appropriate designs. "If it's a Victorian house, you want a Victorian-type gate so it looks like it came with the house and wasn't added on."

About 90 percent of his work is custom and mostly obtained through word-of-mouth. He often works late into the night to meet deadlines. That's when he is occasionally visited by what he half seriously suspects is the ghost of a blacksmith past. All of a sudden the door will fly shut. When he goes to check, there's no wind and no one there. Once as he was cursing in frustration, an ox yoke fell off the wall as if telling him to shut up and keep trying.

But he considers the alleged ghostly visitor a good omen. The spirit would probably lose interest in someone who lacked the enthusiasm and commitment Darold has for preserving the past through the older methods of blacksmithing.

Darold Rinedollar, blacksmith

48

(detail)

(detail)

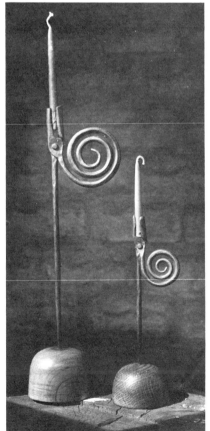

Flower Petal Gate *(above)*
An example of the artist's gates, which are made in the 100-year-old tradition in a forge with leather bellows. The gate starts with a 20′ straight bar of steel; each piece is measured, cut, and worked into shape by hand on the anvil. Each gate is designed to fit individual needs.

Price: $400 (as shown, excluding shipping)
Size: 3′6″ x 32″ (as shown)
Weight: 60 lbs.

Rattail Rush Light *(left)*
These were originally used in 17th century Europe to burn reeds or rushes soaked in oil. The candle is held in place by the weight of the tail. The bases are Missouri oak or cherry.

Price/Size: small (8″)—$20 (without base), $25 (with base)
large (12″)—$25 (without base), $30 (with base)
Weight: 1 lb.

D.A. Rinedollar
P.O. Box 14
Augusta, MO 63332
(314) 228-4583

Brochure available.
Commissions accepted.

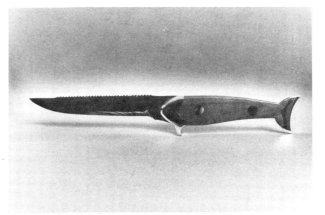

Food Chopper

Handle is Missouri black walnut burl, attached with brass cutlery rivets. The blade is fashioned from old saw blade material and re-heat-treated to hold a very sharp edge. Best suited for kitchen chores.

Price: $85
Size: 4⅜" x 4" x ⅛"
Weight: 5½ oz.

Fish Knife

Fish-shaped knife with brass bolster guard and tail piece, and Missouri black walnut handle inlay. The blade is ¹⁄₁₆" 440c stainless steel and holds a razor edge for filleting, while the top edge is effective for sawing through bone or scraping scales.

Price: $225
Size: 9" x ½" x ¹⁄₁₆"
Weight: 3 oz.

Dale H. Case
R.R. 1, Box 146
Bevier, MO 63532
(816) 775-2286

Brochure available.
Commissions accepted.

Fireplace Tool Set
Handforged from ½″ steel bar. One-piece design eliminates loose handles. Arms of the floor stand are graceful, while heavy base provides stability and catches ashes. Includes 36″ poker, replaceable broom, and deep 32″ shovel. Other sizes and styles available.

Price: $240
Size: 38″ x 15″ x 9″ (approx.)
Weight: 24 lbs. (approx.)

Don Asbee
Route 2, Box 6
Highway 28 West
Bland, MO 65014
(314) 646-3657

Brochure available.
Commissions accepted.

Neck or Patch Knife
Sample of a small knife, used in the early 1800s, that could be worn around the neck in a sheath or encased in a black powder shooter's bag. The handle is deer antler, the blade Norwegian steel. A sheath can be made at an additional charge.

Price: $18 (3" blade), $21 (4" blade)
Size: 6" x 1" x ½"
Weight: 4 oz.

Charles and Wanda Duren
Box 22
Arrow Rock, MO 65320
(816) 837-3408

Commissions accepted.

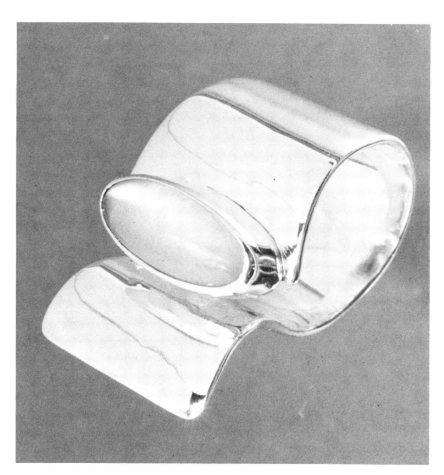

Design for Two Fingers with Moonstone

Made from a sheet of sterling silver and handformed. The moonstone, bezel set, is on top of one finger. The metal then curves around the finger and comes up to lay on top of the neighboring finger.

Price: $90
Size: 1" x ¾" x 1 cm.
Weight: 12 gms.

Marilyn S. Snow
4326 Belleview, No. 2
Kansas City, MO 64111
(816) 561-3948

Commissions accepted.

Tree Frog Ring

Original, handcarved frog ring in 14 kt. yellow gold (½ troy oz.). Can be made in sterling, white gold, with stones set in eyes, with warts, and with curled tongue. Specify ring size.

Price: $495
Size: 1" x ½"

Doug Feakes
Route 1, Box 118-C
Falcon, MO 65470
(417) 668-7724

Commissions accepted.

All jewelry is sterling silver and cast in the lost wax method.

Dove Necklace

Price: $70
Size: 16 mm. x 24 mm. x 4 mm.
Weight: 4 gms.

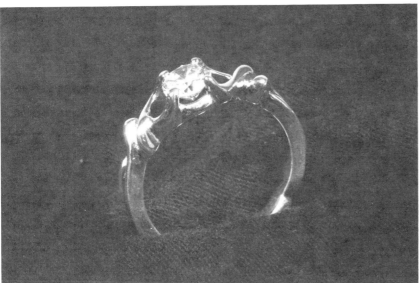

Birthstone Ring

Set with 5 mm. cubic zirconia in white, blue, yellow, red, green, deep amber, champagne, pink, or purple. Other stones available. Sizes 4½ to 7½.

Price: $90 (and up, depending on stone)
Size: 22 mm. x 21 mm. x 6 mm.
Weight: 3 gms.

Heartband

Sizes 5¾ to 8.

Price: $70
Size: 19 mm. x 7 mm. x 19 mm.
Weight: 5 gms.

Randy Wright Estes
3715 Wisconsin
Joplin, MO 64801
(417) 624-9291

Commissions accepted.

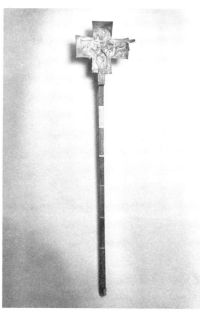

Wall Piece
Wall altar piece with electroformed copper and laminated walnut with Nu-Gold, copper, and nickel silver between units of walnut.

Price: $300
Size: 3' x 8" x 4"
Weight: 3 lbs.

Bracelet
Sterling silver bracelet constructed with reticulated areas.

Price: $250
Size: 3" diameter x ¾" x ³⁄₁₆"
Weight: 5 oz.

Necklace
Sterling silver necklace with cast units and constructed chain. Handcut jade stones in bezel mounts.

Price: $180
Size: 18" chain, 10" drop

Robert Pringle
P.O. Box 234
Columbia, MO 65205
(314) 882-3555

Commissions accepted.

These items are cast in the lost wax process.

Heron Vase

This bronze vase has stylized heron handles and a cattail deeply engraved on one side. All phases, from sculpting to patina, are done by the artist.

Price: $625
Size: 12" x 9" x 3½"
Weight: 11 lbs.

Tadpole Spoon

Sterling silver spoon with a vermeil gold bowl is a baby spoon for a pollywog who is not quite a frog, a serving spoon, or a display piece.

Price: $145
Size: 1" x 6" x 1"
Weight: 2½ troy oz.

Robert E. Allen
408 E. 13 St.
Carthage, MO 64836
(417) 358-8322

Commissions accepted.

Kitchen Utensil Set

Handforged set uses traditional blacksmithing skills. The handles, rack, and fork are iron with hammer-raised bowls of brass. Set includes spoon, fork, ladle, skimmer, spatula, and rack. A variety of styles are available.

Price: $205
Size: 14-16" long
Weight: 5-6 lbs./set

Dan Siglar
315 S. Lawn
Kansas City, MO 64124
(816) 231-6633

Commissions accepted.

Large Hunting Knife

This is the style originally crafted in the mountain man, black powder period. Antler handle is butted with brass with bowie-type guard. Handfitted sheath.

Price: $45
Size: 2½' x 1¼" x 10" (5¾" blade)

Medium Upswept Hunter

For general work and skinning, with deer antler handle, cross-cut saw blade, and brass butt and guard. Handfitted sheath.

Price: $35
Size: 1½" x ¾" x 7¾" (4¼" blade)

Small Drop Point Knife

Used for skinning and gutting; a good first knife.

Price: $25
Size: 1" x ¾" x 5½" (2" blade)

Pete Vannatta
R.R. 3, Box 222
St. James, MO 65559
(314) 265-7479

Mounted Confederate Officer

1st Virginia "Black Horse" Cavalry vs. 5th New York Zouaves Civil War regiments in action; 54 mm. scale. Pieces are cast in tin/lead pewter alloy. Painted in lacquer, acrylic and enamel.

Price: $250 per set
Size: 3½" x 2½" x 4"
Weight: 4 lbs.

Union Artillery vs. Confederate Cavalry

Price: $250 per set
Size: 3½" x 4" x 4"
Weight: 4 lbs.

U.S. Army Color Guard: Dress Greens

Modern dress miniatures.

Price: $60 per set
Size: 5" x 2½" x 4"
Weight: 2 lbs.
Price: $35 on individual
        mounted soldier

Ronald Lloyd Wall
Route 1
Frohna, MO 63748
(314) 824-5312

Brochure available.
Commissions accepted.

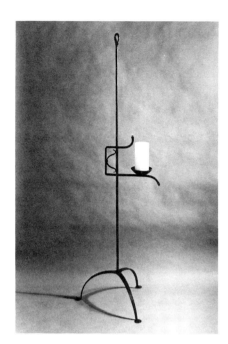

The artist's work includes reproductions, commissions, and original work in metal.

Candle Stand
Handforged steel using traditional techniques. Black finish.

Price: $125
Size: 36" x 14" x 14"
Weight: 2 lbs.

Stan Winkler
204 St. Marys Rd.
Ste. Genevieve, MO 63670
(314) 883-2887

Commissions accepted.

Dragon in Scrolls Fire Poker
(left)
A massive poker forged of six pieces of mild steel welded together by heating in a coal fire, hammering into a single piece, and hammering to shape. The friendly dragon is then forged, chiseled, and chased into shape, and entwined on the handle for balance, grip, and companionship. Beeswax finish.

Price: $65
Size: 38" x 5" x 3"
Weight: 6½ lbs.

Fleur-di-lis Door Knocker
The body of the knocker is forged, split with a chisel, then forged and bent to shape. The knob is forge-welded to a bar, forged and bent to shape, and riveted to the body. Mild steel, beeswax finish.

Price: $50
Size: 8" x 5" x 1½"
Weight: 2 lbs.

Robert C. Patrick
Box 205
Bethel, MO 63434
(816) 284-6687

Brochure available.
Commissions accepted.

Four-Piece Firetool Stand

Tools include shovel, poker, broom, and tongs, and are all finished with a handrubbed linseed oil finish.

Price: $180
Size: 34" x 18"
Weight: 30 lbs. (approx.)

Rectangular Pot Rack

This rack suspends from 2 points; 12 hooks are provided (extra ones available). Will hold up to 24 pots and pans. The finish is a combination of linseed oil and pure beeswax handrubbed to a low lustre.

Price: $80
Size: 16" x 32" x 16"
Weight: 10 lbs.

Bob Crecelius
Route 5, Box 85
Farmington, MO 63640
(314) 756-6015

Commissions accepted.

Veggie Chopper

Hammered out of one of Missouri's most common native materials—the leaf springs of abandoned cars and pickups.

Price: $17.50
Size: ¼" x 4" x 4"
Weight: ½ lb.

Skillet

Forged iron skillet is signed and dated.

Price: $55.50
Size: 2" x 16" x 11"
Weight: 5 lbs.

Shish Kebab

Set of six skewers forged in iron and mounted in wooden base when not in use.

Price: $27.50
Size: 10" x 8" x 2"
Weight: ¾ lb.

Doug Hendrickson
R.R. 1, Box 16D
Lesterville, MO 63654
(314) 637-2576

Commissions accepted.

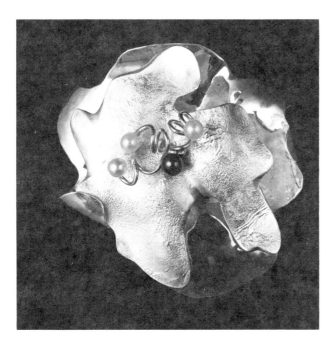

These pins are fabricated from reticulated sterling sheets to give a textured look, with bases forged of a brass sheet, highly polished.

Pin A

Pin is complemented with three pink cultured pearls and one hematite bead on brass wires.

Price: $109.50
Size: 3½" x 4" x ¼"
Weight: 16 gms.

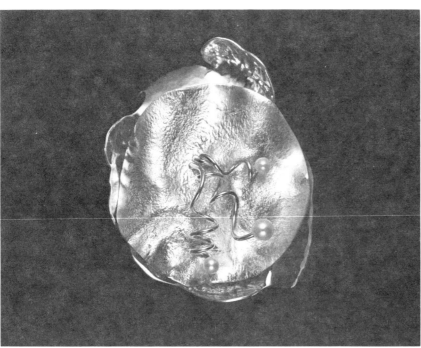

Pin B

Pin is highlighted with three light pink cultured pearls on brass wires.

Price: $100
Size: 2½" x 3" x ¼"
Weight: 14 gms.

Genevieve E. Flynn
5918 Grand
Kansas City, MO 64113
(816) 333-6719

Commissions accepted.

These decorative sculptures are handformed, welded together, and brazed with colored metals for highlights. Wood bases are from Missouri walnut, maple, and oak.

Medicine Man *(top left)*
Price: $1,050
Size: 22" x 7" x 6"
Weight: 10 lbs.

Horned Owl *(top right)*
Price: $2,550
Size: 37" x 30" x 20"
Weight: 27 lbs.

Eagles Nest *(left)*
Price: $2,000
Size: 16" x 18" x 24"
Weight: 23 lbs.

James H. Scorse
R.R. 1, Box 236
Neosho, MO 64850
(417) 624-3594

Brochure available.
Commissions accepted.

dolls

"They're all my babies . . ."

Dolls aren't just for children. If they were, Chintana Moss of Westboro, a tiny burg in the extreme northwest corner of Missouri, wouldn't have the thriving business she does.

She makes porcelain dolls, the kind meant to stand serenely on a shelf rather than be tossed around by children.

Even though they're too beautiful for rough play, that doesn't mean owners don't fall in love with and enjoy the dolls. Because of the patience and care Chintana takes with each one, they almost seem lifelike. "Each one has its own personality as soon as it comes out of the mold," the young artist says.

She has more than 60 different molds for heads, including authentic reproductions of antique dolls from Germany and France. From these she makes female adult dolls, and boy and girl baby dolls.

She came to this country from Thailand to go to school at Tarkio College in Tarkio, Missouri. She then transferred to Northwest Missouri State University in Maryville, where she got a degree in accounting. But after she was married in 1979, she decided she'd rather try her hand at making dolls than be bent over budgets and books.

"I've always loved dolls. I never had one as a child. I guess that's why I love them so much now."

Her first dolls were the baby-type. "When I first started, I made my own hair and painted the eyes. It took so long. So I decided to get eyes and wigs from a doll supply house."

But she does everything else, including the sewing and sometimes designing of the clothes.

She was encouraged to continue in the doll business after winning awards at doll and ceramic shows. Meanwhile, people saw her dolls and the orders started coming in. She made nearly 300 last year. Besides her baby and adult dolls, ranging in height from five inches to two feet, she also makes clothespin dolls. These little creatures are made from four clothespins—one for each leg, one split for the arms and one for the body. She uses wooden beads for the heads and dresses and paints them with the same care as her porcelain dolls.

Just this year she's started making miniature porcelain dolls for doll houses. "I thought they were so cute. So I just had to make some." Even though she doesn't charge more than for her larger dolls, the miniatures are understandably more difficult to produce, since they're only two to five inches tall. "I will get better at it as I go along," she says with the confidence of a skilled perfectionist.

Her husband, a self-employed auto mechanic, helps her when he can. She has to do her doll making around the busy schedule of being a homemaker and mother of her active three-year-old son John. "I have to do the detailed work after he's in bed."

Each doll is the product of much work as well as tenderness. As you watch her paint each eyelash, and use paint remover and redo it until it's just right, and carefully sew and fit each garment, you know if you buy one of her dolls, you're getting the best of her Missouri hands. . . .

Chintana Moss, doll maker

All dolls are signed. The porcelain dolls' molds are poured by the artist.

Clothespin Doll

Body made of wooden clothespin, with moveable arms and legs; handpainted wooden head, face, and shoes; yarn hair (brown, blonde, or auburn); and dressed in old-fashioned print in your choice of color.

Price: $13.50
Size: 8" x 4"
Weight: 3 oz.

Baby Aron

Reproduction of Baby Aron Doll from Seeley's Ceramic Service, Inc. mold. Marked "Germany A 2/0-R." Porcelain head and hands, cloth body, set-in eyes, handpainted hair and face. Long white dress and bonnet are trimmed with lace with pink, light blue, or white ribbon.

Price: $40
Size: 7" x 6"
Weight: 4 oz.

Baby Millie

Reproduction from Joyce Wolf original mold of a portrait doll of Mildred Seeley. Porcelain head, arms, and legs, cloth body, set-in eyes, handpainted face, synthetic hair. Dressed in all white or with pink or blue trim. Also dressed in light blue, pink, and yellow with white trim. Booties included.

Price: $95
Size: 14" x 9"
Weight: 2 lbs.

Chintana Moss
Box 125
Westboro, MO 64498
(816) 984-5656

Phoebe Girl
Cast porcelain doll, handpainted and fired
several times. Glass eyes, quality wig and
costume, Missouri oak base. Signed and dated.

Price: $185
Size: 17" x 8" x 3½"
Weight: 2 lbs., 4 oz.

Jackie Grindstaff
Genevieve Woods Studio
Route 3, Box 407
Ste. Genevieve, MO 63670
(314) 483-2965

Brochure available.
Commissions accepted.

Each creation is handsculpted, including facial detail. Made of Scotchgard treated polyinterlock fabric and handstuffed with 100% polyester fiber, with acrylic fleece hair. Each is attired in individually designed clothing. Signed, numbered, and dated.

Please Mommy?

Mother's face reflects the joys and frustrations of parenthood. Cedar stand.

Price: $47.60
Size: 17" x 11" x 6"
Weight: 15 oz.

2:00 a.m.

Mother rocks baby at 2:00 a.m. in a sturdy redwood rocker.

Price: $48.75
Size: 14" x 8½" x 5"
Weight: 1 lb.

Dorothy Billings
508 W. Locust
Paris, MO 65275
(816) 327-5619

Commissions accepted.

These reproductions are entirely handcrafted by the artist. Stands are included.

Bread Peddler

This doll represents an early 20th century street peddler, and has porcelain head, hands, and feet, a fabric body, a mohair wig and glass eyes. She wears a lined wool coat, polyester-blend dress, and a red flannel petticoat with a pocket containing a penny for luck. Her cloak pockets and tray are filled with miniature breads, pies, cookies, and bakery items.

Price: $400
Size: 20" x 11" x 7"
Weight: 3 lbs.

June Bride

A Jumeau reproduction with porcelain head, composition body, glass eyes, and human hair wig. The dress is polyester silk with over 30 yds. of lace trim and individually sewn seed pearls. She carries a silk flower bouquet and wears a blue garter and gold wedding band.

Price: $675
Size: 28" x 17" x 15"
Weight: 8 lbs.

Kathy Tempel
Route 2, Box 40
Higginsville, MO 64037
(816) 584-2011

Hope
Replica of a Kestner's Gibson Girl, with porcelain head, shoulders, lower arm, and legs; wire frame covered with unbleached muslin body; stuffed with polyester fiberfill. Her features are handpainted, and she has set-in eyes, styled hair, and a satin dress.

Price: $85
Size: 17" tall
Weight: 1 lb.

Yvonne K. Holt
Shy Dolls
Route 3, Box 240B
St. James, MO 65559
(314) 364-8081

Brochure available.

Joanie
A rag doll, fully washable, with hand-embroidered face. Safe even for a baby. Made of broadcloth and pink or blue gingham (specify color choice); polyester fill.

Price: $15
Size: 12" x 11¼" x 2"
Weight: ¾ lb.

Joan Feldkamp
10547 Hobday
St. Ann, MO 63074
(314) 427-1295

Commissions accepted.

J.D.K. Hilda
All-porcelain jointed doll dressed as boy or
girl. Sitting only.

Price: $225
Size: 18"
Weight: 4 lbs.

K ☆ R Pouty
Porcelain head, with 15-piece, jointed
earthenware body. Dressed as boy or girl.
Stands or sits.

Price: $225
Size: 20"
Weight: 4 lbs.

Susan Mullen
316 B-2-A, Route 1
Sparta, MO 65753
(417) 278-3310

Commissions accepted.

These reproductions of old German dolls are signed and dated. Eyes,
hair, and clothing colors may vary unless specified.

"Every bird looks like it could take off and fly . . ."

His birds look so real, people think they're stuffed. But they're not. Alan Gibson of Dexter is a woodcarver, not a taxidermist.

What astounds people is his attention to detail. He painstakingly carves the shaft of each feather and paints it to match perfectly Mother Nature's soft muted tones.

"I try to make every bird look like it could take off and fly," he says proudly.

Once he perched a newly carved quail atop the cage of the live one he'd used as a model. His mother came to visit and wondered who had let the bird out.

He uses live or mounted birds if possible as models for his works. If not, he copies from photographs he's taken or found in one of his many ornithology books.

One of his most dramatic pieces is an eagle that's just captured a bass. The eagle's wings are extended and eyes are fixed on its prize catch. One talon pierces the fish's back. The fish's mouth gapes as if from pain and shock.

This piece depicts so well what Alan is trying to achieve with his art. It's full of action, not just a carved block of wood—a slice of nature captured forever.

Alan, 30, is a self-taught artist with artist blood in his veins. His mother is an art teacher and his sister is a commercial artist. He first tried his hand at carving while managing an art gallery in Dexter eight years ago. His first piece was a miniature killdeer plover.

"I worked my tail off on it," he says of the piece, which he carved out of walnut. He has since switched to jelutong, a wood imported from Malaysia, that's softer and easier to carve, yet which has a consistent grain. For the primary and tail feathers, he uses inserts of harder woods like walnut and maple.

"People like to touch the birds. They won't break easily if they're not made of one solid piece of wood."

He first sketches the bird, because he's also a flat artist, and then proceeds to carve. "I don't use a pattern. I just go by feel." He gets the details with a single-edged razor blade and a wood burning tool, for which he has several tips.

Most of the 50 works he's done are custom-ordered and sold by word-of-mouth out of state. "I've got a collector in Florida. And I've got three collectors in Michigan. I've got birds in Texas, Oklahoma and Georgia as well as Missouri . . . and other states I can't remember."

He is now out of the gallery-managing business and supports himself primarily by making custom-ordered furniture. For example, a local doctor just contracted with him to make a table out of a piece of walnut.

He hopes someday, though, to be only one-quarter furniture maker and three-quarters bird carver.

But regardless of what he creates, Alan Gibson is four quarters artist.

Alan Gibson, woodcarver

Turkey
Price: $1,500
Size: 1/3 life-size
Weight: 15 lbs.

Pelican
Price: $4,000
Size: life-size
Weight: 100 lbs.

Quail
Price: $1,000 for the pair
Size: life-size
Weight: 5 lbs.

Alan Gibson
721 W. Bain
Dexter, MO 63841
(314) 624-4092

Commissions only.

All these examples of the artist's work are handcarved from the Malaysian wood jelutong and painted with acrylic paint. Prices vary according to species and/or pose.

Pennsylvania Dutch Wool Spinning Wheel
Made of Missouri walnut with natural color. Handpropelled.
Moveable spindle base is secured to the table by a wooden bolt
and handnut for tautness of driving band. Rim of wheel is bent
from 1½" wide by ¼" thick strip, overlapped and spliced by
tapered joint.

Price: $300
Size: 60" x 60" x 19" (42" diameter wheel)
Weight: 30 lbs.

John M. Hodge
621 Mt. Auburn Rd.
Cape Girardeau, MO 63701
(314) 334-4373

Chest of Drawers

Inspired by a 600-year-old Chinese chest. The slight angle of the sides gives this piece a solid stance, and the light-colored maple and oak keep it from being too visually heavy. The oak in the side panel is spalted. Drawers are built with handcut dovetails.

Price: $1,750
Size: 53" x 40" x 18"
Weight: 80 lbs.

Rita's Desk

A small, "fall front" desk made of Missouri cherry, with curved, handcarved legs contrasting to the straight, angular lines of the top. Size and arrangement of drawers and shelves can be built to order.

Price: $1,450
Size: 37" x 28" x 13"
Weight: 60 lbs.

Michael Bauermeister
Route 1, Box 310
St. Clair, MO 63077
(314) 629-1775

Commissions accepted.

Continuous Arm Windsor Chair
Price: $390 (excluding freight)
Size: 37″ x 19″ x 21″

Loopback Windsor Sidechair
Price: $250 (excluding freight)
Size: 37″ x 17″ x 18″

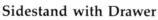

Sidestand with Drawer
Based on Shaker design, table is cherry with pegged mortises and tenons and tapered legs. Drawer has poplar sides, hand-dovetailed to front and back. Knob is handturned.

Price: $230 (excluding freight)
Size: 28″ x 20″ x 20″

All furniture has a handrubbed oil finish. The chairs are made of oak for the spindles and back, which are handriven for strength. The seats are poplar, which is handshaped by draw knife and spokeshaves, and the legs and stretches are hard maple and individually turned. All joints are wedged and glued. Prices include crating but not shipping. Pieces are shipped freight collect.

Patrick Nelson
Ch'ien Creative Hardwood Furniture
Route 2, Box 331
Fulton, MO 65251
(314) 642-7776

Brochure available.
Commissions accepted.

Blue Gill Perch

Life-size perch is handcarved from Ozark walnut. The eyes are glass and the base walnut.

Price: $75
Size: 5½" x 2¼" x 8"
Weight: 12 oz.

Jimmie R. Jones
Route 1, Box 77
Noel, MO 64854
(417) 436-2417

Commissions accepted.

Cheval Mirror

Handcrafted from white pine, these may be used as vanity mirrors or to display a favorite doll.

Price/Size: $15 (11" x 6" x 6½", 1 lb.)
$17.50 (14" x 7½" x 7", 1½ lb.)
$20 (17" x 8½" x 8½", 2 lbs.)
$22.50 (20" x 9½" x 9", 2 lbs.)
$27.50 (23" x 10½" x 10", 3 lbs.)

Marianne Seelinger
Route 3, Box 148-A
Pleasant Hill, MO 64080
(816) 987-2965

Brochure available.
Commissions accepted.

Lap Desk

Painted to order.

Price: $44
Size: 3″ x 14½″ x 9″
Weight: 2 lbs.

School Lap Desk

Each floral design original; no two alike unless specified.

Price: $67
Size: 4½″ x 17″ x 11″
Weight: 3¾ lbs.

These lap desks are made from pine and handfinished to a warm patina glow. They are portable, convenient for papers, stationery, photos, and bills, and can be personalized. Each has fresh floral original painting that can be specified.

Dodie Eisenhauer
P.O. Box 11
Daisy, MO 63743
(314) 266-3642

Commissions accepted.

These collectibles are made with dowel and glue construction and natural finish in tung oil or urethane. All have burned-in signature and are numbered.

Fire Engine

Crafted in solid Missouri walnut and featuring swivel spotlight, helmets, axes, fire-extinguishers, rear storage compartments, and removable ladders and hoses.

Price: $78
Size: 4⅝" x 4½" x 13¼"

Pick-Up Truck

Made of walnut, pine, and cedar, and featuring steerable spoke wheels, adjustable windshield, and operating tailgate. Other woods available.

Price: $98
Size: 6¼" x 5¼" x 12½"

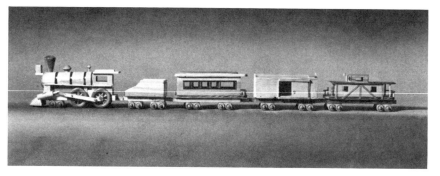

Train

Made of pine, spruce, and maple with working drive linkage and doors. Complete with tender, boxcar, work car, and observation car.

Price: $327.50
Size: 5-7½" x 4¾" (each),
      overall length is 52"

Don Jacobs
Route 1, Box 149
Harrisburg, MO 65256
(314) 874-8178

Commissions accepted.

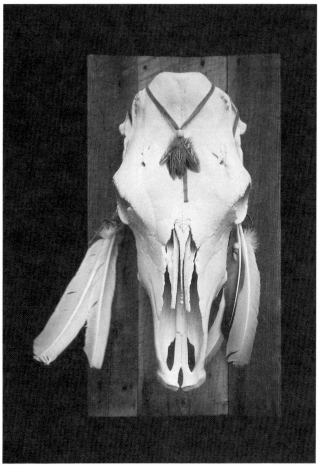

Indian Spirit Wall Sculptures

These pieces are created from animal skulls gathered from Missouri woodlands and pastures. One-of-a-kind sculptures.
Price: $75   Size: 18" x 10" x 9" (approx.)   Weight: 5 lbs.

Gertie Lowe
1705 A St.
Blue Springs, MO 64015
(816) 229-9522

Commissions accepted.

Bread Box

Solid red oak box can be ordered with natural or rustic finish and with ceramic or brass knobs.

Price: $58.68
Size: 12" x 16" x 20"
Weight: 15-18 lbs.

David Durreman
Route 1, Box 273AA
Crocker, MO 65452
(314) 736-2605

Wren
This life-size bird is handcarved in wood and handpainted with oil colors. Signed.

Price: $45
Size: 5″ x 6″ x 6″
Weight: 5 oz.

Clem Wilding
R.F.D. 1, Box 19
Berger, MO 63014
(314) 834-5414

Commissions accepted.

Handcarved in Missouri basswood, these waterfowl are painted in acrylic and coated with clear acrylic to protect the finish.

Mallard Pair

A lifelike rendition of the well-known waterfowl "Old Greenhead," with detailed carving and lifelike colors.

Price: $730 (per pair)
Size: 7" x 5" x 12" (each)
Weight: 4 lbs. (each)

Pintail Pair

Detailed featherwork highlight this colorful pair.

Price: $730 (per pair)
Size: 7" x 5" x 16" (each)
Weight: 4 lbs. (each)

Blue Wing Teal Pair

Distinctive in his blue hue and white-blazed cheek, this little duck and his mate are well known to duck fanciers.

Price: $795 (per pair)
Size: 6" x 5" x 10" (each)
Weight: 4 lbs. (each)

Sam and Carol Burns

P.O. Box 452
Gainesville, MO 65655
(417) 679-4418

Commissions accepted.

Red Oak Door Mat
Guaranteed not to blow off your porch, of Missouri red oak, glued, nailed and soaked in linseed oil for protection. Dirt and snow scrape off through slats.

Price: $37   Size: 1½" x 13½" x 26"   Weight: 8 lbs., 8 oz.

Wooden Kaleidoscope (*left*)
A fractured reality scope showing images at both ends. Specify oak, walnut, or cedar.
Price: $12
Size: 1¼" x 1¼" x 4¼"
Weight: 2 oz.

Red Oak Cooling Racks and Trivets (*right*)
2-loaf racks; nontoxic finish.

Price: $8
Size: 10¾" x 11" x ¾"
Weight: 12 oz.

Steve and Sharon Henderson
Wooly Woods Woodworking
Route 3, Box 166
Alton, MO 65606
(417) 778-6451

Brochure available.

Ratchet Pine Candle Stand

Copy of an old lighting device, with twin candles raised and lowered on a wood ratchet. Made from pine and other Missouri woods. Slides are wood-pinned and joints are mortised and wedged. No nails are used. Signed.

Price: $108
Size: 22″ x 9″ x 2″
Weight: 2 lbs.

Handcrafted Pine Candle Box

Used around 1700 to hold candles, this replica is made from Missouri oak, walnut, cherry, and old pine when available. Rubbed hand finish. Signed.

Price: $85
Size: 4½″ x 5¼″ x 13″
Weight: 2½ lbs.

German-Style Harvest Tressel Table

Each table designed for the owner out of Missouri pine, oak, or walnut. Legs and stringer are handcut, mortise and tenon jointed, with carved pins holding top cleats and top. Price depends on length, design, and finish. Signed. Contact artist for delivery/shipping charges.

Price: $950-$1,800

Robert G. Hostkoetter
Route 3, Box 82
Marthasville, MO 63357
(314) 433-5669

Commissions accepted.

Wood Mosaics

This chess or checkerboard can be played on and hung on the wall by its hook when not in use. The board shown is made of walnut, birch, wenge, amaranth, bubinga, and cedar. Signed.

Price: $150
Size: 7/8" x 23" x 23"
Weight: 4½ lbs.

Robin Tucker
Route 1, Box 70
Spickard, MO 64679
(816) 485-6251

Spice Cabinet

Solid oak with four drawers, cabinet top has open teardrop with towel bar at bottom. Behind the veneer-paneled door are two shelves. Handrubbed oil finish.

Price: $80
Size: 21″ x 13½″ x 3¼″
Weight: 12 lbs.

Jewelry Chest

Made of solid Missouri black walnut with black walnut insert with holes for rings. Made of fully interlocking joints. Includes 6″ mirror on lid. Handrubbed oil finish.

Price: $105
Size: 5″ x 12″ x 8″
Weight: 5 lbs.

Jim McDonald
24 Spruce
Farmington, MO 63640
(314) 756-3239

Commissions accepted.

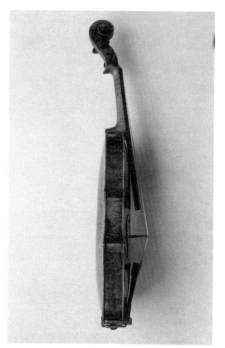

Violin
Price: $5,000
Size: 23½" x 8½" x 4"
Weight: 1 lb.

Made from artist's own pattern and design. These violins are all handcarved and inlaid. All woods are select and dried for a minimum of 10 years (maple for the back, sides, and scroll, spruce for the belly, and ebony for the trim). Varnish made by the artist for tone and beauty. Violin tone rich and full.

Geoffrey J. Seitz
3806 Loughborough
St. Louis, MO 63116
(314) 353-1312

Commissions accepted.

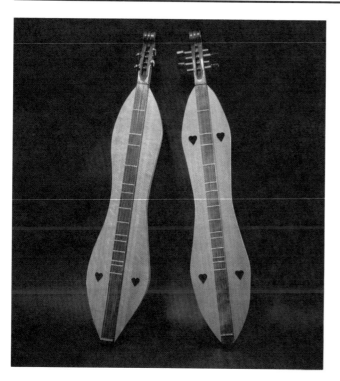

Mountain Dulcimer
Made with hand tools of solid cherry with quarter-sawn spruce tops. Available with guitar-type tuning or traditional wooden pegs. Comes in other shapes and woods.

Price: $350
Size: 37" x 7" x 2¼"
Weight: 3 lbs.

R.M. Archambeault
R.R. 1
Kidder, MO 64649
(816) 575-2573

Commissions accepted.

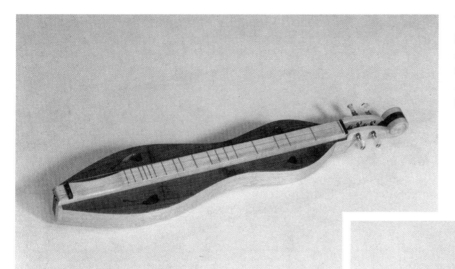

These mountain dulcimers are made of solid wood with no laminates. The back and soundboard are book-matched. Each comes with a beginner's instruction book.

Dulcimer B
Made with geared pegs and a handcarved scroll on the peghead. Birdseye maple with walnut soundboard.

Price: $275
Size: 3" x 7-8" x 34"
Weight: 3-4 lbs.

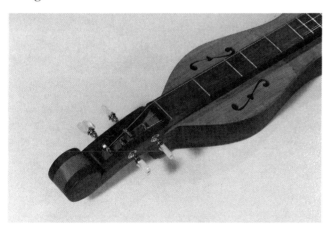

Dulcimer A
Made with friction pegs and assorted sound holes. Crafted from solid woods, including walnut, cherry, maple, and koa.

Price: $225
Size: 3" x 7-8" x 34"
Weight: 3-4 lbs.

Dulcimer C *(bottom)*
This model has geared pegs, handcarved peghead scroll, inlay in sound holes, and mother-of-pearl inlay in strum hollow.

Price: $325
Size: 3" x 7-8" x 34"
Weight: 3-4 lbs.

Bill Van Dusen
Route 2
Hale, MO 64643
(816) 565-2937

Rocker *(above)*
Solid walnut, caned replica of 19th century rocker. Old-style joinery used. High lacquer finish.

Price: $475
Size: 38" x 24" x 28"
Weight: 30 lbs. (approx.)

Gun Cabinet *(opposite page)*
Cabinet is solid black walnut with no veneers, with old-fashioned joinery used throughout. Holds 10 guns plus drawers for pistols or gun accessories. Drawers mounted on phonograph slides for precision. Satin finish.

Price: $2,700
Size: 90" x 36" x 16"
Weight: 200 lbs. (approx.)

Victor L. Hilber
East Park Lane
Shelbyville, MO 63469
(314) 633-3598

Commissions accepted.

Decorative Waterfowl Carvings

Price: $250-$400
Size: 6" x 7-8"
Weight: 5 lbs.

Made of Missouri basswood, these carvings achieve anatomical accuracy with traditional carving chisels, specialized woodburning techniques for texture, and coloring with acrylic washes. All birds are native to Missouri and require between 120 and 150 hours of labor.

Miniature Waterfowl Carvings

Price: $50
Size: 2" x 2"
Weight: 1 lb.

Shelby G. Jones
217 Binder Dr.
Jefferson City, MO 65101
(314) 635-4598

Brochure available.
Commissions accepted.

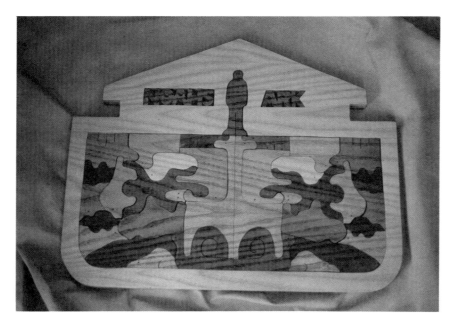

Noah's Ark Puzzle
Contains 37 pieces stained in different colors. Made of ¾" ash plywood and finished with a polyurethane finish that is safe for children.

Price: $40
Size: 16½" x 21" x 1"
Weight: 4 lbs., 12 oz.

Glenn and Barb Gregory
Route 1, Box 76AA
Armstrong, MO 65230
(816) 273-2360
(816) 248-2248

Brochure available.
Commissions accepted.

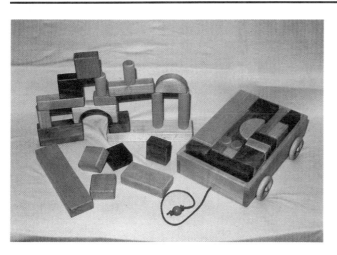

Wagon/Block Set
These smooth blocks are easily stacked, sturdy, and include all the basic shapes. Finished with natural, nontoxic oil, wagon and blocks are 100% colorful Missouri woods such as maple, black walnut, cherry, and oak. No two sets exactly alike. Free replacements of any block that breaks. Specify dark or light wood.

Price: $45 ($40 F.O.B.)
Size: 4½" x 9" x 13½"
Weight: 7 lbs.

Dottie Sherman
Route 1, Box 227
Columbia, MO 65201
(314) 442-5032

Commissions accepted.

Kitchen Stool
Crafted in solid Missouri oak and available in
Early American or dark walnut stain.

Price: $50
Size: 11″ (high) x 10″ x 24″
Weight: 10 lbs.

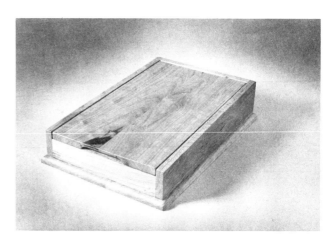

Lap Desk
Solid Missouri oak, walnut, or cherry, with
small compartment for pencils and pens.

Price: $75
Size: 4″ x 12″ x 17″
Weight: 7 lbs.

Terry Wilks
Box 268, Route 1
Centerville, MO 63633
(314) 689-2577

Commissions accepted.

Wooden Puzzle Stool

A virtually indestructible stool with letters in bright colors so that the child can learn to spell his/her own name and learn colors at the same time. Letters are as educationally correct as possible. Made with oak legs and poplar top. Specify name.

Price: $29.50
Size: 8¾" x 8½" x 11½"
Weight: 5 lbs.

Joann Johannes
Johannes Wood Products
3230 Ridge Rd.
Jackson, MO 63755
(314) 243-8242

Brochure forthcoming.
Commissions accepted.

Acoustic Guitar

These guitars are handcrafted with emphasis on durability, tonal quality, and playability. Backs and sides may be rosewood, mahogany, maple, koa, or walnut; soundboards typically sitka spruce; necks one-piece mahogany or laminated maple; fingerboard and bridges ebony or rosewood. Electric and classical guitars also available.

Price: $600 (and up)

Jeff Bush
1803 Monroe St.
Columbia, MO 65201
(314) 443-6039

Price list available.
Commissions accepted.

McKenzie Strad Violin
Copy of McKenzie Stradivarius of 1685, this violin is of 4/4 size in red-brown, with eight coats of oil varnish. It has a two-piece back, sides, and neck of curly maple; spruce belly; ebony fingerboard, pegs, chin rest, tail piece, and button; and Flexicor strings. Signed and dated. Price determined by quality of sound.

Price: $1,500-$3,000
Size: 24" x 8⅛" x 2½"
Weight: 1 lb.

Harold I. Beasley
Route 1, Box 123
Naylor, MO 63953
(314) 354-2291

Brochure available.
Commissions accepted.

Designed Bells

Created on a wood lathe and finished to a soft lustre with four coats of a lacquer-type product. The wood of Missouri oak, walnut, cedar, and cherry give each bell a distinctive design and sound. Specify wood choice. Other styles available.

Price: $5.80
Size: 5⅛" x 1⅛-1⅜"
Weight: 1 oz.

Bertram A. Cowley
Route 2, Box 94
Vandalia, MO 63382
(314) 594-2126

Brochure available.
Commissions accepted.

Solitary Sandpiper Decoy
Handcarved from western cedar, with an acrylic finish wiped down on the back and wings to expose the natural grain. It features relief-carved wings and simulated glass eyes. The base is a piece of cedar root.

Price: $54
Size: 10" x 9" x 3"
Weight: 1 lb.

Spotted Sandpiper Decoy
Handcarved from basswood with acrylic finish, simulated glass eyes, and relief-carved wing outlines. The base is a split piece of local white "paperbark" birch.

Price: $54
Size: 8½" x 7½" x 3"
Weight: 1 lb.

Dowitcher Decoy
This type of decoy is widely known as a Hudson Dowitcher. It features an old square-cut nail for the bill and simulated glass eyes. It was carved from white pine, given an acrylic finish, and mounted on a native oak knurl.

Price: $45.
Size: 10" x 7" x 3"
Weight: 1 lb.

All birds are also available in an "Antique Series," which features a distressed-aged appearance.

Jim Barksdale
Box 35
Steelville, MO 65565
(314) 775-2027

Commissions accepted.

Hummingbird
Made of solid Missouri black walnut, each is handfinished. No two are exactly alike.

Price: $14.95
Size: 1½" x 5½" x 1¼"
Weight: 1 oz.

Snowbird
Handcrafted of Missouri black walnut and handrubbed to a satin sheen that enhances the wood grain. Each will vary slightly and possess its own personality.

Price: $14.95
Size: 2" x 4½" x 2"
Weight: 3 oz.

Nick Carras
Route 9, Box 482
Springfield, MO 65804
(417) 862-9683

Commissions accepted.

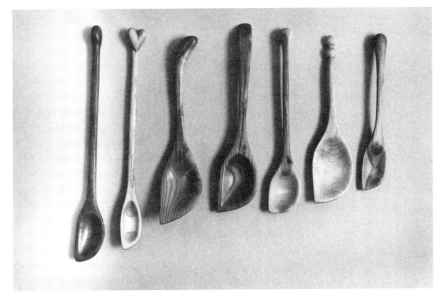

Square-Cornered Stirring Spoon

Price: $28.50
Size: 12-15″ x 2-3″ x ½-1″
Weight: 1-2 oz.

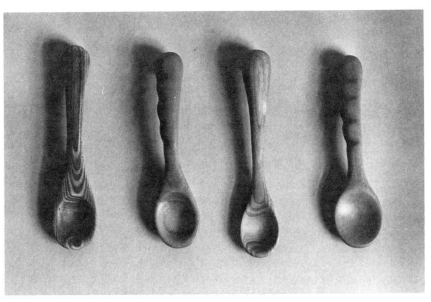

Baby Spoon

Price: $14.50
Size: 5″ x 1″ x ½-¾″
Weight: ¼-½ oz.

These spoons are made with rare, traditional handcarvings of Ozark hardwoods. Each is unique, designed to accent the beauty of the wood. Naturally finished with edible oil. Also available in your choice of wood or spoon design.

Ted Berger
Route 3, Box 129
Willow Springs, MO 65793
(417) 962-3204

Commissions accepted.

Each time the artist sells a piece of her work, she plants a tree to replenish her source.

Hooded Merganser
Handcrafted from select Missouri hardwoods, this bird is double-sealed and signed. Suitable for indoor or outdoor use. Many items available.

Price: $18.95
Size: 6½" x 11½" x ⅜-½"
Weight: 1 lb.

Margaret Morris
Woodwoman
3403 Barberry Ave.
Columbia, MO 65202
(314) 445-5363

Brochure available.
Commissions accepted.

Milking Cow Whirligig
Made of solid pine stock with cedar propeller. Each done by hand, including control wires and brackets. The man and arms handpainted, the cow silkscreened. The faster the wind blows, the faster the arms pump and the tail bobs up and down.

Price: $25
Size: 5" x 7" x 8"
Weight: 12 oz.

Peter Brown
Route 4, Box 216B
Forsyth, MO 65653
(417) 546-4472

Brochure available.
Commissions accepted.

Fruit and Nut Bowls
Handturned on lathe with five coats of handrubbed satin
finish. Available in laminated walnut/maple combination, solid
walnut, and solid cherry, as well as in other sizes and shapes.
Do not clean with water. Signed.

Price: $19
Size: 2½-3" high, 7½" diameter
Weight: 1 lb.

Hans W. Neumann
R.R. 3
Mexico, MO 65265
(314) 581-0176

Life-Size Birds

Price: $85 (wren, chickadee),
$125 (cardinal)
Weight: 6 oz.

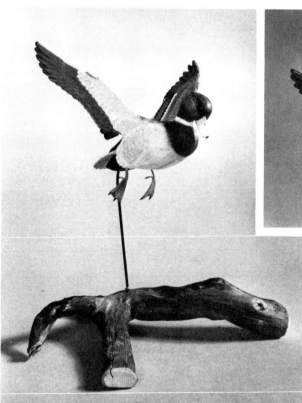

(detail)

Miniature Mallard Duck in Flight

Price: $295
Size: 10" x 8" x 6"
Weight: 6 oz.

*These handcarved birds are of Missouri hardwoods and handpainted.
Feathers are carved and veined and realistic glass eyes are used. Each
stand on driftwood collected by the artist near her home in the Ozarks.
Other birds and male/female pairs are available.*

Marjorie Sutton
Route 2, Box 64
Gerald, MO 63037
(314) 764-2663

Coffee Table

Made of Hawaiian koa wood with gently flared legs and curved apron. Rails have exposed mortise/tenon joinery. Matching end tables available.

Price: $500
Size: 12" x 36" x 21"
Weight: 35 lbs.

Jewelry Box

Made of exotic bubinga wood, this box has lid lifts mortised into the lid frame, and inside dividers and a lift-out tray. Tung oil finish.

Price: $200
Size: 3⅝" x 10⅝" x 7½"
Weight: 7 lbs.

Side Table with Drawer

Made of select Missouri hickory with handcarved walnut drawer pull. Top rails are dovetailed into legs, and bottom rails are pinned mortise/tenon. Tung oil finish.

Price: $450
Size: 28" x 24" x 17"
Weight: 30 lbs.

Tom Cole
Route 1, Box 219
Harrisburg, MO 65256
(314) 875-1417

Commissions accepted.

Wooden Butter Churn
Old-style churn made of white oak and
hooped with four metal bands. Wood is left
natural with no finish. Dasher is of the cross
design.

Price: $35
Size: 30" x 8½" x 15¼"
Weight: 11 lbs.

Doug Bratcher
1330 Clayview
Route 6, Box 145
Liberty, MO 64068
(816) 781-0347

Commissions accepted.

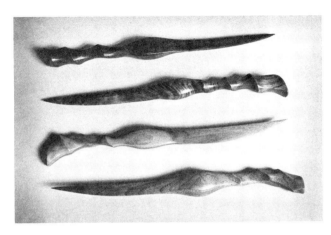

Letteropeners

Available in straight grain walnut, cherry, purple heart, tulip wood, and burl walnut.

Price: $17.50 (and up)
Size: 9-11" x ⅞" x ⅝"
Weight: 1-1½ oz.

Gavels

Come with clatterboards.

Price: $95 (oak, straight grain walnut), $125 (burl walnut)
Size: 10-10½" x 3½" x 1⅜-1⅞"
Weight: 6-8 oz.

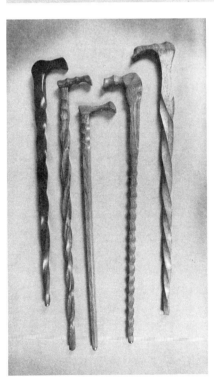

Fancy Canes

Length of cane is cut to order; the average length is one-half your height. A brass ferrule is seated on the tip, and the handle is attached with a steel pin, seated with epoxy. Available in oak, tulip wood, birds eye maple, cherry, zebra wood, and burl walnut with plain and spiraled shafts.

Price: $95 (and up)
Size: custom height x 1¾" x 1"
Weight: 1 lb.

The designs for these items are roughed in with a belt sander, then filed and sanded by hand. They are polished with three types of finish.

Gregory Aguirre
2406 W. Broadway
Columbia, MO 65202
(314) 445-2923

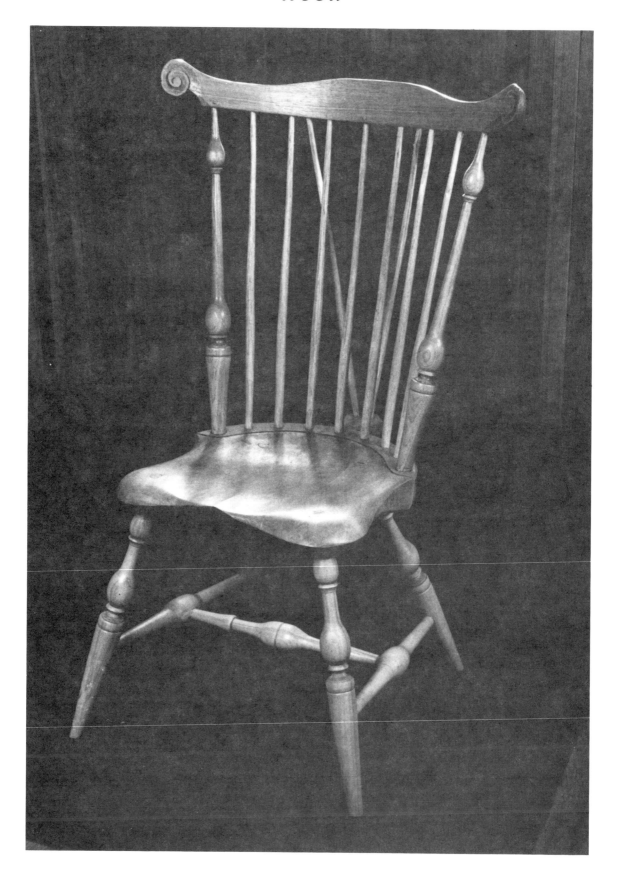

Continuous Arm Windsor Chair *(top left)*
An interpretation of a style popular in New England in colonial times. The bow and spindles are white oak, riven from a log and shaped while green, then dried.

Price: $340 (excluding shipping)
Size: 37½" x 24" x 23"
Weight: 12 lbs.

Bowback Windsor Arm Chair *(top right)*
Design is based on a chair made in Maryland circa 1800, although other features have been added.

Price: $335 (excluding shipping)
Size: 37½" x 23" x 18½"
Weight: 14 lbs.

Fanback Windsor Side Chair *(opposite page)*
Similar to chairs made in Connecticut in the late 18th century. The spindles and back posts are hickory.

Price: $275 (excluding shipping)
Size: 39½" x 24½" x 21½"
Weight: 10 lbs.

Larry Ayers
R.R. 2
Knox City, MO 63446
(816) 434-5419

Brochure forthcoming.
Commissions accepted.

glass

"He asserts his independence through crafts . . ."

There's a certain spirit that lives in Missouri. It's a spirit of free will and independence that leads many never to feel fulfilled until they're working for nobody but themselves and doing what they know best.

This spirit creates many quality artisans. One of the beginners is Leland "Micky" Burkett of rural Sturgeon. He likes his independence. So he's embarked on a new career venture—making rock lamps.

These colorful lamps resemble stained glass lamps, but the look is richer. The rocks, which come from all over the world, add designs unobtainable with glass.

He learned how to make the lamp shades from his grandfather in Indiana, a creative man who came up with the designs and techniques on his own. "Ethan Allen asked him to make 100 for their store. But he turned them down because he just wants to make them for fun," Micky said.

But Micky, who rebuilds wrecked cars for a living in addition to occasionally doing home construction work, wants to see if he can help support his family—wife Tina and baby son Cale—with the lamps. He makes three different sizes of table lamps as well as a large shade for a hanging lamp, suitable as a dining room fixture.

The rocks he's used so far have been obtained from a dealer in Indiana. But he plans to replenish his supply at a larger dealership in Mississippi. The rocks must be translucent when sliced.

From the slices he cuts out the designs he wants. He then fits them into a wooden mold and solders the pieces together with lead and copper. His wife, who runs a beauty shop out of their home, helps him assemble the designs.

Micky is new in the craft business. And with the determination of a Missourian, he plans to make his mark in it.

More traditional approaches to the use of light as a basis for artistic expression are represented by other artisans in this section. The oldest form of stained glass work uses blown or rolled glass in a frame of lead strips soldered together at the joints. This technique is most often seen in flat pieces like windows.

Other artisans use different kinds of glass and assemble them in more flexible forms by using thin strips of copper foil. The foil-edged pieces are then soldered together in a variety of two- and three-dimensional shapes, such as panels or windows, lamp shades, or glass sculptures.

No matter what the approach, the final product shows the beauty created by transforming light with form, color, and line.

Leland Burkett, lamp maker

Shades

Price: $175-$300
Size: 7½″ x 8″ (small)
Weight: 1½ lbs.

Shade C

Price: $600
Size: 7½″ x 11½″
Weight: 3 lbs.

Shade D

Price: $1,200
Size: 10″ x 20″
Weight: 6 lbs.

These lampshades start with translucent rocks that are sliced into ¹⁄₁₆″ thick pieces, coated with resin for strength and shine, and cut to size. The edges are wrapped with copper foil, the shade is assembled in a wooden jig and the pieces soldered together. All saws, patterns, and jigs are handmade by the artists. Bases are not included.

Leland and Tina Burkett
Route 1, Box 34-K
Sturgeon, MO 65284
(314) 687-3703

Ruby Throat Hummingbird

Window is crafted from antique and art glass using the copper foil technique. Wood frame is cherry with natural finish and polyurethane. Window one of "Birds of Missouri" series (11 other birds available). Frames also available in oak and walnut, and custom sizes can be ordered.

Price: $120
Size: 15¾" x 13¾" x 1½"
Weight: 3 lbs.

Bird Dutch Door

This interior door is made from cherry and select native Missouri hardwood, finished with handrubbed polyurethane and waxed. The top half has approximately 300 pieces of antique and art glass. Door also available in oak and walnut and in custom sizes.

Price: $1,150 (excluding freight)
Size: 72" x 34" x 1½"
Weight: 40 lbs.

Sergai Mars
Mozark Estates
Reynolds, MO 63666
(314) 689-2586

Commissions accepted.

Missouri Dogwood
Painting is kiln-fired on white opalescent glass until proper depth of color is obtained and then framed with stained glass.

Price: $135
Size: 14″ x 12″ x ¼″
Weight: 1½ lb.

Calla Lilies
A variety of textured glass gives this window depth. It is assembled using the copper foil technique, and the frame is crafted of Missouri oak.

Price: $200
Size: 26″ x 15″ x 1″
Weight: 7 lbs.

Oriental Study (*opposite page*)
Nearly 300 pieces are assembled using the copper foil technique. Antique glass in background was mouthblown in Germany, and the glass in the flowers is a dichromatic glass that changes dramatically with different light. Frame crafted from Missouri walnut.

Price: $350
Size: 27½″ x 22½″ x 1″
Weight: 9 lbs.

Katherine E. Howser
905 Collier Lane
Fulton, MO 65251
(314) 642-7128

Commissions accepted.

The artist creates each design on paper then transfers it to the glass and handcuts the design. The piece is then sandblasted. This work can be hung or used as windows.

Battling Owls

Two sandblast-carved glass panels mounted in oak or walnut frame. Frame contains interior lighting. Limited edition of 20. Specify wood.

Price: $1,250
Size: 36" x 36" x 5"
Weight: 125 lbs.

Two Fish

Single glass panel is combination of sandblast carving and surface etching.

Price: $200
Size: 18" x 24" x 2"
Weight: 10 lbs.

Maiden of the Bubbles *(opposite page)*

Three sandblast-carved glass panels mounted in native oak or walnut frames. Frame contains interior lighting. Limited edition of 20. Specify wood.

Price: $2,500
Size: 42" x 36" x 5"
Weight: 150 lbs.

J.W. Skeeba
525 N. 25th St.
St. Joseph, MO 64501
(816) 233-3995

Brochure available.
Commissions accepted.

Harvest Lamp

This lamp features a blue-mauve mottled art glass background with dark blue and green grape jewels. Leaves are green, blue-green, and bronze-red iridescent. Corner panels are bronze iridescent. Also available with red grapes and buff-bronze leaves. Includes lamp base.

Price: $185
Size: 20½" x 10"
Weight: 7 lbs.

Work is crafted from copper foil and is signed.

Wild Harvest

A late summer glimpse of birds and wild grapes in 28 colors, crafted in foil from several types of glass in 270 pieces. Use as window or hanging panel. Sent motor freight, collect.

Price: $412
Size: 51" x 19¾"
Weight: 12 lbs.

Elizabeth Osburn
R.R. 2, Box 506
Harrisonville, MO 64701
(816) 884-3889

Commissions accepted.

(detail)

Stained Glass Kaleidoscope
This kaleidoscope is made of glass and mirrors, but can be ordered using jewels, bits of glass, or anything you might want to incorporate into the color wheel. Smaller sizes available.

Price: $55
Size: 10" x 4" x 4"
Weight: 2 lbs.

(detail)

Faye Hutchison
Route 2, Box 460
Seymour, MO 65746
(417) 935-4985

Commissions accepted.

"He captures the honesty and simplicity of rural America . . ."

Most artwork depicting the Amish people shows buggies, bonnets and barefoot boys in suspenders—a cartoonish and superficial look at their lifestyle.

But not the art of Joel Chrisman, 39, of Laredo. He admires the way this culture gives so much while taking so little from the land. He tries to show his respect by depicting what's inside their homes, their barns, their yards—but without showing the people themselves.

His main medium is pencil, which seems to lend the necessary soft and delicate yet simple touch to what he draws—a dining room table ready to be set, a bridle and harness hanging in the barn, an auction showing only the tops of the straw hats of the Amish in attendance.

"To me it's a challenge to try and make my drawings lively and colorful without using color. It's a challenge to get a full range of tones in black and white."

Joel, who looks Amish himself with his full beard and rather stern expression, first became interested in these people eight years ago. That's when he decided to move to Laredo, a town of less than 400 people. There's a large settlement of Old Order Amish nearby. He identified with their lifestyle because he was in the midst of giving up an office job in a big city, Denver, to return to his roots and try to make a living from his drawing.

Joel agrees with the way the Amish refuse to use pesticides and herbicides in their farming. He and his wife Cynthia try to grow as much of their own food as they can. He feels there's much modern people can learn from the Amish ways.

With his drawings, he tries to transmit a feeling for their lifestyle. "I show the things in their life, the things they use or the places where they work."

His other drawings do this, too. They show a fresh look at small town life. For example, he has a series on the inventions of the man who runs the local garage.

Most of his drawings are available in 9-by-12-inch lithograph prints as well as note card form. In addition, he does a wide range of commercial art projects and commissioned drawings.

"I do mainly buildings, farms and houses. People like me to draw the farm where they grew up or their house. They give copies as Christmas presents."

With his six-foot frame bent over a drawing board in the middle of America, this big, burly man captures the simplicity and honesty of rural life as few others see it.

Joel Chrisman, artist

120

Amish Scenes

These reproductions of the artist's drawings of the Old Order Amish Community in and around Jamesport, Missouri, are available in a series of limited-edition prints (250 each, signed and numbered), and are printed on archival, acid-free paper.

Price: $22.50

Size: 11″ x 14″ (sheet), 9″ x 12″ (image)

Joel Chrisman
Route 1, Box 7
Laredo, MO 64652
(816) 286-2475

Commissions accepted.

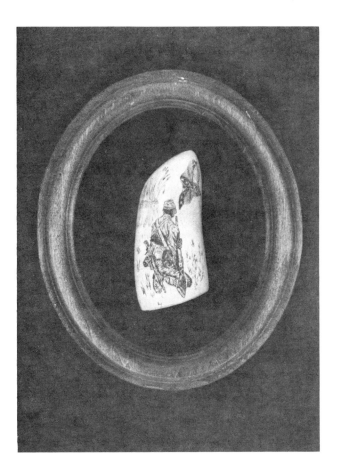

No two pieces are alike. Commissions range from $50 to $600, depending on size, material, color, and type of display.

Confederate Soldier
Black and white scrimshaw on deer antler. Each piece is signed.

Price: $100
Size: 3½″ x 1½″

Fish
Stipple technique scrimshaw on fossil ivory. Variety of wildlife available in black and white or in color, whichever will best depict the subject.

Price: $250 (color)
Size: 3½″ x 2½″

Tony Young
8144 N.E. 50th St.
Kansas City, MO 64119
(816) 452-3725
(816) 861-4700 (ext. 583)

Commissions accepted.

Winter Farm Scene

Photograph capturing the romance and nostalgia of rural life. Mounted.

Price/Size: 11″ x 14″—$20 (unframed), $45 (framed)

16″ x 20″—$40 (unframed), $65 (framed)

Weight: 2 lbs. (11″ x 14″), 4 lbs. (16″ x 20″)

The Inquisitive One

Photograph of a male racoon looking for love. Mounted.

Price/Size: 11″ x 14″—$20 (unframed), $45 (framed)

16″ x 20″— $40 (unframed), $65 (framed)

Weight: 2 lbs. (11″ x 14″), 4 lbs. (16″ x 20″)

John L. Ebeling
Ozark Wilds
Versailles, MO 65084
(314) 378-6430

Commissions accepted.

Time Plaza Building, Kansas City, MO

Woolf Brothers Courtyard, Kansas City, MO

Carriage Ride

The 6" tiles come with a masonite back or framed in oak. A combination of bottling the glazes and silk-screening creates the raised glaze, giving the tiles a rich, etched look. All are $15 (single tile) and $25 (in oak frame). The artist can do special commissions such as buildings and corporate logos.

Carolyn Payne
Payne Creations
4829 N. Antioch Rd.
Kansas City, MO 64119
(816) 452-8660

Brochure available.
Commissions accepted.

Missouri Birds and Wildflowers

Handpainted ceramic tiles can be used in combination with plain tiles or individually as trivets or in frames. Over 15 wildflowers and 15 birds available and listed in brochure.

Size/Price: $9.95 (4¼" square), $14.95 (6" square)
$18.95 (4¼" x 8½")

Lee Hamilton
Route 1
Miami, MO 65344
(816) 852-3214

Brochure available (send $2).
Commissions accepted.

Charcoal Portraits

Contact the artist for a complete price list. Pastels, oils, and acrylics also available.

Price: $24.95 (and up)
Size: 3" x 5" to 16" x 20"

Betty Jo Alkire
Historic Taneywood
Rockaway Beach, MO 65740
(417) 561-8106

Brochure available.
Commissions accepted.

Squaw Creek

Tavern sign is oil on old wood, with dark background, gold lettering, golden sky, and muddy blue water. Personalized signs can be made.

Price: $145 ($165 personalized)
Size: 20" x 30" x 1"
Weight: 4-5 lbs.

Quilts for Sale

Primitive scene in oil on door panel in green, white, red, blue, and yellow.

Price: $145
Size: 15" x 31" x ¾"
Weight: 3-4 lbs.

Country School

Primitive scene in oil on old wood breadboards. Painted in soft green and gold with white schoolhouse.

Price: $65
Size: 13" x 20" x 1"
Weight: 1-2 lbs.

Jo Thompson

1625 Crescent Dr.
St. Joseph, MO 64506
(816) 233-8406

Commissions accepted.

Lithographic Print
Numbered and signed print on high-quality textured stock.

Price: $12.50
Size: 12" x 18"
Weight: 3 oz.

Foldover Note Cards with Envelopes
Each shrink-wrapped package contains 20 cards and 21 envelopes.

Price: $5.50
Size: 4⅝" x 6¼"
Weight: 5 oz.

Postcards
Each shrink-wrapped package contains 20 cards.

Price: $6.50
Size: 4⅝" x 6¼"

"Phelps County Sod Busters" was sketched by the artist while attending the team mule competition at the Ozark Extravaganza in Vichy, Missouri. Each item is printed by the artist.

Kevin D. Carlile
7 Burgher Dr.
Rolla, MO 65401
(314) 341-2946

Brochure available.
Commissions accepted.

fine art

The Artist views each painting as not only a description of a particular place, but also a feeling about that place. The buyer may choose a subject generally, such as "A Missouri Barn," "Southeast Missouri Landscape," etc., or specifically, such as "the House on 232 Johnson St., Anytown, MO," etc. Suitability of the subject for watercolor is at Artist's discretion.

Average fee for framed 22" x 28" original watercolor is $185, plus preliminary design fee of $15-$85.

Dusk at Shepherd Mountain Lake

Edgar Watertower, Arcadia Valley

The House Across the Tracks, Arcadia Valley

Kip DeVore
361 S. Main
Ironton, MO 63650
(314) 546-7606
(314) 546-3465

Commission work only.

The artist takes a sketchbook wherever she goes, even helping with the farm work, to produce pencil drawings on a variety of subjects. Prices begin at $50.

Daffodils

Carol I. Ellis
Route 1, Box 128
Amity, MO 64422
(816) 449-5514

Commissions only.

Indian

The imprimatura for this painting is silkscreened onto canvas, and the canvas is then heightened with white, a step that produces the glowing quality of the "Old Masters" technique. Pigment is then applied in thin glazes until desired richness and depth of color is achieved, and final darks and lights are added. Edition limited to 1,000. Each is signed and numbered.

Size/Price: 8" x 10"—$150 (flat), $155 (stretched), $180 (stretched and framed)
12" x 16"—$200 (flat), $207.50 (stretched), $250 (stretched and framed)
20" x 24"—$300 (flat), $310 (stretched), $375 (stretched and framed)

Lynn M. Chapman
1406 Rifle Terrace
St. Joseph, MO 64506

Brochure available.
Commissions accepted.

Woodburned Eggs

Eggs are "art-in-the-round," woodburned in a variety of styles with an electrically heated pen on wooden eggs. Prices vary with detail of egg.

Price: $100-125 (per egg)
Size: 2½" x 1½"
Weight: 2 oz.

Cale Kenny
Box 55
Skidmore, MO 64487
(816) 939-2365

Brochure available.
Commissions accepted.

baskets

"Tucked in the Ozark forests lives an artist . . ."

Tucked in the Ozark forests, in a house that can't be seen from the road and can't be reached except at the end of a long, two-rut drive, lives a woman who's found contentment in life.

Jennifer Weston, 36, of rural Ava, loves weaving baskets. She loves it so much she sits and does it just about everyday when she's not tending garden, preserving food, baking bread or doing some upkeep on the old frame house and 80 acres she shares with her friend, Joanne Olszewski.

Jennifer used to be an art teacher in Grand Rapids, Michigan. But she and Joanne decided to get away from the chaos of the city and lead a simpler life in the country.

"This is more like it was when I was growing up," she says of her adopted Missouri home. Her father was a county extension agent and she spent her early years in rural Michigan.

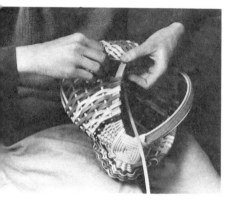

But try as one might to be subsistent, there's still a need for money coming in. So that's why she makes baskets. Joanne, a former business teacher, does all the money managing for the business they call "Gathering Root Basketry."

"I got hooked with the first basket," she says. She took basket weaving classes while still living in Grand Rapids.

Jennifer's sturdy baskets are based on designs of pioneers and native Americans. An example is her egg basket with its short handle, so it won't swing, and two compartments, so the eggs won't hit one another. She weaves with vines she gathers on her property, such as the grape and buckbrush. But to produce volume she relies on imported rattan strips.

Her long slender fingers become one with the supple strips she maneuvers under and over the basket spokes. She has to stop every few minutes and hold the basket up for inspection. "You have to keep shaping the basket to keep it symmetrical."

She uses natural dyes when she can. "I use sumac berries for gray, log wood for purple, brazilwood for pinks and walnuts for brown." But for blues she has to rely on commercial dye because it's more colorfast.

She does some teaching of basket weaving and continues to take classes herself. She subscribes to several basketry newsletters and does research on baskets at libraries she visits.

Weaving baskets allows her to stay home and enjoy nature.

"I feel sorry for people who live on the land and never enjoy it—people who spend their lives commuting to work."

Her calm expression and soft green eyes are those of a woman who's found meaning and joy in living.

Jennifer Weston, basket weaver

132

Melon Basket
Named for its shape, this basket has a wild grapevine handle and weavers dyed from black walnut hulls.

Price: $38.50
Size: 11" x 10" x 10"
Weight: 7 oz.

Sewing Basket
Roomy, lidded basket has "curls" inspired by Native American basket decoration. Accent colors available in choice of: wine/rose, walnut brown/gold, or country blue/barnyard grey.

Price: $47
Size: 6½" x 11" x 11"
Weight: 10½ oz.

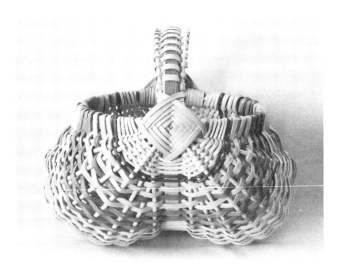

Egg Basket
Based on a basket crafted by hill people, with a double bottom to prevent eggs from rolling. Woven handle. Accent stripes. Available in country blue/denim/walnut brown, silver grey/dark plum/light plum, or walnut brown/ peach/salmon.

Price: $38.50
Size: 9" x 10½" x 8"
Weight: 6½ oz.

Jennifer Weston
Route 5, Box 176
Ava, MO 65608
(417) 683-3610

Commissions accepted.

Flat-Bottomed Egg Basket
Traditional double butt design made of split cane with twined handle. Stained with natural walnut stain. Can be woven in your color choice.

Price: $35
Size: 9″ x 10″ x 5″
Weight: 6 oz.

Carla McFarland
1615 Amelia
Columbia, MO 65201
(314) 443-6204

Commissions accepted.

Large Gypsy Basket

This design, of European-Appalachian origin, has two flared sides extending downward, with its handle fixed to the rim with a "God's Eye," and is lined with palm thatch from south Texas. Wood rim and handle, imported rattan for weavers and ribs. Available in plain or smoked.

Price: $120
Size: 21" x 18" x 21"
Weight: 2 lbs. (approx.)

Small Gypsy/Wine Basket

Made of rattan stained in fermenting grapes. Color is a variegated lavender pastel mosaic that can fade with prolonged exposure to the sun.

Price: $42.50 ($32.50 plain or commercial dye)
Size: 8" x 8" x 10"
Weight: 1 lb. (approx.)

Smoked Cat Basket

White oak oval rim from southern Missouri and a triple handle (commercial) are woven with cane and reed, with flat reed used for strength. Basket is smoked using green hickory wood for softer color contrasts and as a preservative. Good for garden work or fireplace logs if the cat refuses to sleep in it.

Price: $80
Size: 12" x 12-20" x 13"
Weight: 1 lb. (approx.)

Ken and Nina Johnson
R.R. 1, Box 200-A
Hermann, MO 65041
(314) 486-3920

Commissions accepted.

Wicker Buggies

An 1800s-style buggy designed for a child's stroll with his/her favorite doll or teddy bear. Signed and dated. Made of wood-reed wicker with a solid wood frame. Specify light or dark blue, red, white, oak-stained, or unfinished. Other colors and styles available.

Price/Size: stained—$65 (19" x 6" x 12", 1 lb.), $85 (26" x 9" x 19", 3 lbs.); add $5 for colors

Cheri and Mike Russell
Wicker Fixers
Route 1, Box 349
Ozark, MO 65721
(417) 485-6148

Brochure available.
Commissions accepted.

Pamela S. Walker
1714 Lakewood Dr.
Columbia, MO 65202
(314) 474-4928

Commissions accepted.

Nontraditional Potato Basket

Woven of hand-dyed reed and/or splint, with hickory, ash, or oak rims. Diameter of the rim determines size and price of the basket. Prices range from $14.40 (3") to $189.75 (28").

Gathering Basket *(above)*

Reed basket with oak rims and handles. Colors range from solid walnut to natural. Also available in natural with accent of walnut, colonial blue, red, or evergreen. All under 1 lb.

Price/Size: $10 (6"), $17 (8"),
$25 (10")
$35 (12"), $45 (14")

Moses Basket *(left)*

Reed basket most popular as a doll's bed. Available in natural or smoked reed.

Price/Size: $17 (8" x 12"), $25
(10" x 15")
$35 (12" x 20")

All baskets are signed and dated and are available in a variety of sizes.

Ruth Petsel
P.O. Box 154
Ironton, MO 63620
(314) 546-3164

Commissions accepted.

Ozark Gizzard-Shaped Egg Baskets

Price/Size: $25.00 (8″ hoops, 6 oz.)
$32.50 (10″ hoops, 8 oz.)
$40.00 (12″ hoops, 10 oz.)

Replicas of a traditional design, these baskets are handcrafted using hardwood hoops with reed ribs and weavers. Available with walnut hull stain, pine stain, or natural, and may be trimmed with a variety of colors. Signed.

Robert C. Zimmerman
P.O. Box 825
West Plains, MO 65775
(417) 256-9703

Commissions accepted.

Gathering Basket

Sturdy basket made from flat rattan reed, with oak-stained oak handle. Each is unique, changed by the addition of different color and size reed. Can be stenciled.

Price: $39.95
Size: 18" x 12" x 10"
Weight: 9 oz.

Debbie Reber
P.O. Box 379
Ellington, MO 63638
(314) 663-7414

Commissions accepted.

Hearth Basket

In years past, this reed basket was probably used for carrying kindling to the hearth. Signed and dated.

Price: $39.95
Size: 17" x 18" x 10"
Weight: 1 lb.

Debra Rayfield
Route 2, Box 327
Ellington, MO 63638
(314) 663-2269

Commissions accepted.

Missouri Black Walnut Caned Stool
Also available in oak, ash, or other hardwood. Made with ¾″
diameter dowels. Legs are 1¼″ square. Handcaned.

Price: $50
Size: 9″ x 12″ x 9″

William J. Ernst
Loutre Valley Enterprises
Box 113
Montgomery City, MO 63361
(314) 564-2493

Commissions accepted.

Country Market Basket

Adapted from square-bottom apple basket, each is woven of natural weavers with hand-dyed accents of country blue. Handles of white oak; size of handles determines size of basket. Signed and dated.

Price: $29.50
Size: 12" x 8" x 5" (approx.)
Weight: 8 oz.

Susan M. Minor
Route 2, Box 275A8
Marshfield, MO 65706
(417) 468-5744

Heart Baskets

Handwoven ash-reed baskets available in blue, rose, red, chestnut, and mauve.

Price/Size: $11.50 (6½" x 6")
$14.50 (9" x 8")

Janet Lee Perry
310 Collier
Centralia, MO 65240
(314) 682-5970

Commissions accepted.

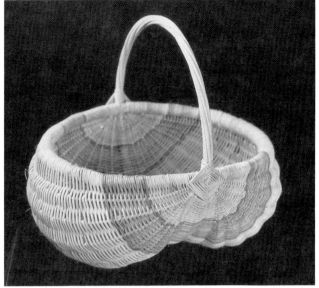

Hen Basket
Tightly woven rattan with a band of golden-tan (dyed with the Missouri "weed," St. John's Wort). Could be used for an arrangement or as a handbag.
Price: $37.50 Size: 10" x 9" x 5"

Egg Basket
A ribbed rattan basket in traditional "fanny" shape. Decorative bands are colored with onion skins and edged by a strip dyed with walnut hulls.
Price: $50 Size: 11½" x 10½" x 5" (12½" long)

Gathering Basket
Rattan basket with seagrass and bands of greenish-yellow (dyed with Missouri tickseed) decorating each side.
Price: $50 Size: 5½" x 11" x 5½" (13½" long)

Gloria Craker
Route 2, Box 27D
Monett, MO 65708
(417) 235-5082

Photographs available.
Commissions accepted.

"Her hands are never idle . . ."

The devil can't find work for Sue Gerard because her hands are never idle.

When she's not shaping pots on one of her wheels, the 72-year-old woman is swimming, biking, writing free-lance articles or doing chores on her farm outside Columbia.

But it's her pottery that earned her a spot in the "Best of Missouri's Hands" catalogue, specifically her sculpted small white clay figures and her miniature pots. "If I wanted to get rich, all I'd make is miniatures," she claims. But the depth of her creativity needs many more outlets. She also makes all sizes and sorts of jugs, vases, lamp bases and pottery dinnerware to order.

She fires all her work either in her wood kiln—just like the pioneers used—or her electric kiln.

The wood kiln is right outside her workshop, a converted shed warmed by a wood stove so she can work year-round. About three times a year she fires the kiln for the 12 hours it takes the pots to get cooked just right.

She uses a salt glaze just like the pioneers did, too. "They used what they had," she says. This gives a gritty, earthy texture to her creations, including the miniatures.

She's been working the clay since 1972, when she retired early as a college swimming teacher because of a trapped nerve in her neck.

Her knowledge of anatomy, acquired from a master's degree in physical education, helped her in creating her "white people," as she calls the four-inch-high figures she makes from white clay so fine it looks like porcelain. She digs it in a roadbank near her home.

When she first shows the figures to you, she introduces them by name.

"This is Aunt Bess," she says of a bonneted woman kneeling at a spring dipping water. "She wasn't really my aunt, but everybody called her that. Whenever you came to visit, she'd offer you a nice cold drink of water from her spring—not a can of pop like we do today." Sitting alongside the spring is a tiny frog. "There was always a frog at her spring," Sue chuckles.

She goes on through the rest of her people: Eli splitting rails, Helen making apple butter, Hazel giving Harold his Saturday night bath, and poor Sarah, who got something caught in the wringer when she leaned over too far one washday. . . .

There are 70 different ones, all figures from her past—either relatives or neighbors of her parents—each made individually and not from a mold.

She likes the white clay, not only because of its beauty, but also because it can be worked so fine that it allows her to make the apron strings, bows and other details her figures require for authenticity.

The next batch of white clay she readies "will last me the duration," she says with the confidence of someone who'll meet her Maker with a long list of accomplishments to show.

Sue Gerard, potter

Miniature Pottery Pots and Jugs

Traditional early American miniature pots and jugs made from Missouri's stoneware clay, turned on a wheel, burned in a wood fire, and glazed with salt. Each has been completed by flames, ashes, and smoke from the wood fire. Variety of sizes and colors. Initialed.

Price: $5.50
Size: 1.5 cm. x 4 cm.
Weight: 3 oz.

Little People of Boone's Lick Trail

Sculpted from moist clay that the artist digs in Boone County near the old Boone's Lick Trail. Minnie washes on the board, Uncle John sleeps on the job, Hazel bathes Harold, Emeline cards wool, Sadie knits. Special orders available. Named, numbered, and signed.

Price: $24 (and up)
Size: 4" x 2.5"
Weight: 5 oz.

Sue Gerard
Folk Art in Clay
Route 2
Columbia, MO 65201
(314) 442-2809

Brochure available.
Commissions accepted.

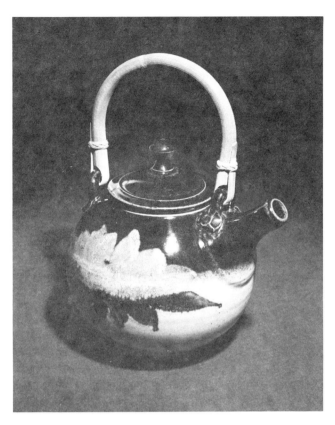

This functional stoneware is made primarily of Missouri clay, fired first to bisque, then glazed and refired to cone 10, and is safe for the oven, microwave, and dishwasher.

Teapot
Black tenmoku glaze on top, white glaze on bottom, with iron and rutile decoration. Cane handle.
Price: $45
Size: 10" x 8"

Serving Bowl
Black tenmoku glaze with white inlaid glaze decoration. Also available in porcelain.
Price: $18
Size: 8" diameter

Casserole
Black tenmoku and green celadon glazes with iron brushwork decoration.
Price: $40
Size: 8" x 10"

Stephen L. Ayers
615 Center
Hannibal, MO 63401
(314) 221-6960
(314) 221-6026

Commissions accepted.

Sun
A sculpted planter cast in high-fired ceramic and stained in buff or brown.

Price: $35
Size: 14″ x 13″ x 4″
Weight: 2 lbs.

Janet Wyse
Rock Creek Farm, Inc.
Route 1, Box 260
New Bloomfield, MO 65063
(314) 491-3630
(314) 751-2343

Brochure forthcoming.
Commissions accepted.

Jug

Concentric banding on shoulder with pulled and applied handle. Can be made in a variety of shapes and sizes based on traditional forms.

Price: $40
Size: 10½" x 5½"
Weight: 3½ lbs.

Bread Bowl

This bowl has a thick rim, straight sides, and flat base, with finger marks for decoration. It is typical of German potters' work in Hermann, Missouri, in the 1800s and was often used for mixing and raising bread. Bowls can be made in other shapes and sizes. Some are slip trailed for decoration.

Price: $25
Size: 4½" x 11¼"
Weight: 4 lbs.

The wheel-thrown redware is glazed with nontoxic clear to milky colemanite glaze. Some clay is dug by the potter from a creek bank near Starkenburg.

Dennis J. Weber
P.O. Box 338
Rhineland, MO 65069
(314) 236-4412

Commissions accepted.

Carp
This unglazed fish is sculpted of 100% Missouri stoneware clay.
The shape is clay pressed into a mold made by the artist from
his own design. Each fish is then individually finished by
applying additional bits of clay or by incising into the clay.

Price: $50
Size: 4½″ x 4½″ x 13″
Weight: 3 lbs.

Donald E. Tefft
Red Crow Art Studio
6800 James A. Reed Rd.
Kansas City, MO 64133
(816) 353-2886

Commissions accepted.

Steeper for Boiling Potpourri

Wheel-thrown and handcarved steeper. Fill top with water and one tablespoon of boiling potpourri, and votive candle will steam the liquid. Specify blue, white, or green. Sizes may vary slightly.

Price: $28 ($4.50 for boiling potpourri)
Size: 6½" x 4" x 2"
Weight: 1 lb.

Stoneware Mixing Bowls

Handcrafted on treadle wheel and available in two-tone blue and white, green and white, or solid blue, brown, green, or white. Bowls nest for storage.

Price: $72 (per set)
Sizes/Weight: 16-cup (6" x 10" x 5½", 2 lbs., 12 oz.)
              10-cup (4½" x 8½" x 4", 2 lbs., 2 oz.)
              6-cup (3¾" x 7" x 3", 1 lb., 4 oz.)

Meg Fertig
P.O. Box 594
St. Joseph, MO 64502
(816) 364-6779

Commissions accepted.

Earthenware House Ornament
Each slip-casted ornament is painted in detail from your house photo, then handsigned and double kiln fired. Personalization of your choice included.

Price: $22.50
Size: 3½" (round)
Weight: 1-2 oz.

Serena Boschert
714 Washington St.
St. Charles, MO 63301
(314) 946-1874

Commissions accepted.

Charles Dickens Christmas Carollers
Inspired by the classic Christmas story.

Price: $55 (each)
Size: 12½" x 4"
Weight: 8 oz.

Mail Bag Santa and Dear Santa
Mail Bag Santa is modeled on the Santas of the early 1900s. Dear Santa captures the late 1800s.

Price: $58 (each)
Size: 8" x 7-8" x 5-7"
Weight: 8 oz.

Each doll is an original, with no molds used. The heads are sculpted from clay, with the bodies made from muslin-wrapped wire and affixed to wooden bases.

Nancy Lee Wheaton
1513 West Scott Place
Independence, MO 64052
(816) 833-2238

Brochure available.

Emerald Green Bowl

Handthrown stoneware bowl is dishwasher and oven safe.

Price: $135
Size: 7″ x 14½″ x 5½″
Weight: 10 lbs.

Amber Tulip Jar *(opposite page)*

The design was created by using a cut-out pattern with slip brushed over it.

Price: $450
Size: 25″ x 16″ x 24½″
Weight: 45 lbs.

Priscilla Block
1167 Hillside Dr.
St. Louis, MO 63117
(314) 645-1353

Commissions accepted.

These pieces are made from clay body containing native Missouri clay. They are fired to 2180° F. and are signed.

Bird Feeder

Stoneware feeder comes with rot-resistant nylon hanging cord and natural twig perches. Available in four different weather-proof glazes. Signed.

Price: $22
Size: 8" x 6" x 6"
Weight: 1430 gm.

Butter Crock

Stoneware crock in 19th century American pottery tradition. Comes with cobalt-blue decoration on lead-free grey glaze. Dishwasher, oven, and microwave safe. Signed.

Price: $6
Size: 4¼" x 5¼" x 5¼"
Weight: 695 gm.

Set of Four Mugs

Stoneware mugs with generous sized handles for both hot and cold beverages. Dishwasher and microwave safe. Available in four lead-free colors. Signed.

Price: $22
Size: 3⅞" x 3⅛" x 4¾"
Weight: 370 gm. (each)

Lee Ferber
Route 1, Box 16-F
Lesterville, MO 63654
(314) 637-2507

Commissions accepted.

Vase A
Price: $35
Size: 7-8″ x 3″ x 3″
Weight: 1 lb.

Vase B
Price: $45
Size: 8-10″ x 4-5″ x 4″
Weight: 2 lbs.

Zinc crystals are actually grown on the outside of these handthrown porcelain vases in an elaborate firing process. The crystalline structure is unique to each work, but color consistency is possible. Colors include navy, light blue, jade green, mauve, and yellow. Specify color choice. Wooden bases available at additional cost.

Frank Neef
Star Route 1, Box 338
Highlandville, MO 65669
(417) 587-3861

Commissions accepted.

Mug

This 8-oz. capacity mug has a concave neck to help with heat retention.

Price: $12
Size: 4¼" x 4½" x 3¼"
Weight: ¾ lb.

Vase

A graceful, traditional form suitable for holding flowers or grasses, or simply standing on its own. Blue and white glaze.

Price: $57
Size: 11" x 8"
Weight: 5½ lbs.

Teapot

This blue and white, 48-oz. capacity pot has a well-balanced handle and is designed for daily use.

Price: $35
Size: 6" x 10"
Weight: 2½ lbs.

The stoneware clay body of all items contains Missouri fire clay. Each piece is decorated with lead- and barium-free glazes, then fired to 2360° F, and are microwave and dishwasher safe.

Robert E. Putnam
721 E. 63 Terrace
Kansas City, MO 64110
(816) 523-7115

Commissions accepted.

Wizard Bell
Face and hands are unglazed and hair is porcelain. Includes 1″ crystal ball.

Price: $28.60
Size: 9″ x 3″
Weight: 1 lb.

Tower Lamp
This 7-watt electric light makes a good nightlight or accent piece. Tower is natural with glazed roof and details. Electric parts included.

Price: $82.50
Size: 17″ x 6″
Weight: 5 lbs.

These items are wheel-thrown stoneware with handsculpted detail and are available in navy blue, blue/violet, or dark brown.

Melissa Hogenson
R.R. 1, Box 114
Ethel, MO 63539
(816) 486-3471

Brochure available.
Commissions accepted.

Butter Keeper

Pack butter (or margarine) in the top and place water in the bottom. When closed, the water seals the butter compartment and the evaporation keeps the butter cool enough to not need refrigeration, but soft enough to spread. Lead-free and nontoxic.

Price: $20
Size: 5" x 4"
Weight: 2 lbs.

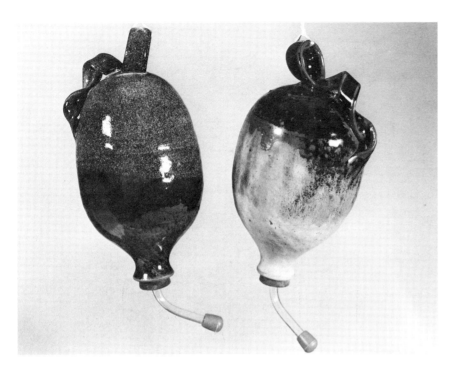

Handthrown stoneware pieces are sturdy and functional. All come in a variety of colors.

Hummingbird Feeder

The feeder has a decorative coil for hanging and an easily removable spout for filling or cleaning. Fill with sugar syrup and enjoy the hummingbirds. Dishwasher safe.

Price: $14
Size: 8" x 4"
Weight: 2 lbs.

Open Flame Lamp

Lamp has decorative clay ribbon handle for easy carrying. Fill with scented lamp oil for fragrance and soft light.

Price: $14
Size: 5" x 5"
Weight: 1 lb.

Susan Minyard
Route 3, Box 93A
Mansfield, MO 65704
(417) 741-6630

Brochure available.
Commissions accepted.

Double Ring Fountain

This two-piece stoneware fountain is assembled from wheel-thrown parts, then glazed and accented with airbrushed coloring oxides before firing. A small recirculating pump is housed in the base. It can be used indoors or outside during warm weather. The fountain has a brisk and rushing sound and holds approximately 5 gallons of water. Contact the artist for shipping charges.

Price: $600 (excluding freight)
Size: 32" x 19¾"
Weight: 34 lbs.

Deanna Nichols
2615 N. Bell
Avondale, MO 64117
(816) 452-0880

Commissions accepted.

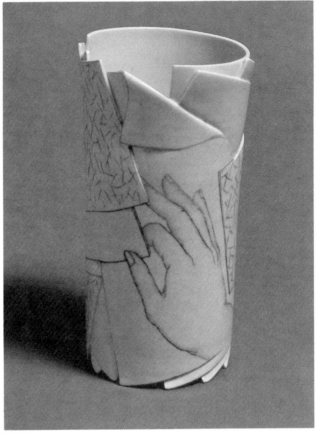

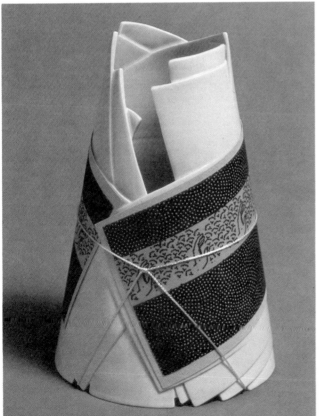

Wrapped in Blossoms *(top left)*
A pattern of blossoms is used both in black underglaze pencil on the porcelain and photocopied onto mylar, tied with a cord.
Price: $195
Size: 8" x 6½"
Weight: 2 lbs.

Pulling It Together *(top right)*
Brown, black, and blue underglaze pencils were used to draw the hand in the act of wrapping the form.
Price: $105
Size: 8" x 4"
Weight: 1½ lbs.

Blossoms and Dots *(left)*
A collage of patterned dots and drawn hands with blossoms was photocopied onto clear, archival-quality mylar, tied with a cord.
Price: $195
Size: 8" x 5½"
Weight: 1¾ lbs.

Linda Mosley
1515 Hialeah
Florissant, MO 63033
(314) 831-9318

Brochure available.
Commissions accepted.

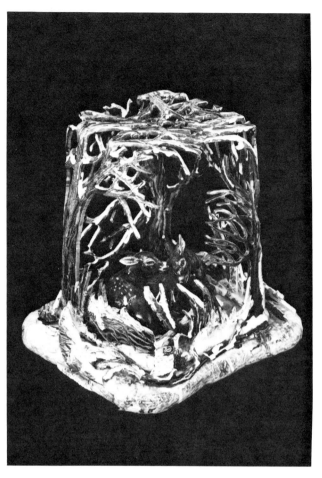

First Snow
Original stoneware sculpture of two young deer in a thicket of trees.

Price: $1400
Size: 11⅛" x 10" x 11¼"
Weight: 1½ lbs.

Autumn Hunt
Original stoneware sculpture portraying the fall colors of Missouri's trees. Trees and figure can be displayed together or separately.

Price: $900
Size: 16⅜" x 10¼"
Weight: 2½ lbs.

Margaret R. Travis and Jasmar
P.O. Box 147
Foristell, MO 63348
(314) 673-2867

Brochure available.
Commissions accepted.

Dinnerware

Porcelain dinnerware is handmade, signed, lead-free, and oven, dishwasher, and microwave safe. Also available in stoneware and terra cotta and in many styles and glazes. Set includes dinner plate, bowl, cup, and salad plate.

Price: $47/place setting (porcelain), $43 (stoneware), $39 (terra cotta)

Baking Dishes

Oval and rectangular stoneware bakers are oven, dishwasher, and microwave safe. Each piece is shaped on the wheel, altered and fired with lead-free glaze, and signed by the artist. Come in many colors and decorations.

Price: $40
Size: 11" x 6" x 4"
Weight: 3-3½ lbs.

Joan Marshall
9825 Shepherds Dr.
Kansas City, MO 64131
(816) 942-5253

Slides, price list, and studio visits available. Commissions accepted.

Container
Stoneware container with decorative lid has potter's fingering marks for interest and is glazed in a range from off-white to brown. Dishwasher safe.

Price: $47
Size: 9" x 7½"
Weight: 4½ lbs.

Storage Jar
High-fired stoneware jar with lid. Natural white and brown glazes. Dishwasher safe.

Price: $42
Size: 12" x 5½"
Weight: 4½ lbs.

Christina Riesberg-Robb
Route 1, Box 174
1451 W. Creed Rd.
Sturgeon, MO 65284
(314) 687-3507

Commissions accepted.

Mixing Bowl and Serving Dish
These dishes are cone 6 porcelain or stoneware with white clay body and white glaze with colorful brushwork. Dishwasher, microwave, and oven safe.

Price/Size: mixing bowl—$34
(8" diameter, x 6")
serving dish—$30
(12" diameter, x 4")

Maddy Fraioli
Box 144, Main St.
Greentop, MO 63546
(816) 949-2648

Brochure available.

Place Setting

Four-piece place setting, hand-decorated with oxides and slips.

Price: $12 (plate), $6 (small plate), $6 (cup), $6 (bowl)
Weight: 6 lbs.

Casserole
Handpulled handles.

Price: $20
Size: 8" x 6" (without lid)
Weight: 2½ lbs.

Jar
The inside and the inside of the lid are glazed to hold liquid; the outer surface is unglazed to emphasize slip decoration.

Price: $20
Size: 6" x 6"
Weight: 2 lbs.

This work is wheel-thrown and hand-decorated, fired to cone 6, and safe for microwave, oven, dishwasher, and refrigerator. Other colors and decorations are available.

Susan D. Speck-Sampson
3021 Campbell
Kansas City, MO 64109
(816) 531-5119

folk art

"Miniature log cabins for tiny porcelain people . . ."

Her dream is to have a log cabin of her own some day. But in the meantime she's making miniature ones for tiny porcelain people to enjoy.

Laura Lee Hicken, 34, of rural Buffalo, started this craft about four years ago and has since given up a profession as a dental technician to devote herself to it full time.

The only criticism of her technique may be that she puts far more time into it than she can ever recover for her price. But she wouldn't have it any other way. It's the attention to detail that makes her work stand out from others.

There's the dulcimer on the wall . . . the apple pie cooling on the window sill . . . the table set with spatterware dishes. . . .

Each time you look at her cabins you see something you've never seen before.

These homesteads, on a scale of one inch to one foot, are typical of what the early Missouri settlers had—one room with a bedroom loft.

In front of the cabin stands mustachioed Pa with feathered hat, overalls, handkerchief in pocket and a piece of straw in his mouth. Ma and Daughter sport colorful dresses with lace and ribbon trim. Bonneted Baby sits at their feet.

Laura makes the dolls from purchased molds. She paints on the facial features and shoes and sews all their clothes.

She diligently does every detail of the cabin, too, from wallpapering to constructing each piece of furniture to stuffing the muslin mattresses and pillows with cotton. She glues each cedar shake shingle on the roof. "I guess there are probably 500. I never count," she grins. She used to glue small rocks onto board for the fireplace and chimney but has since created a mold for this and now makes the fireplace from ceramic and paints each little stone.

In front of the fireplace lies a bear rug with beady eyes and teeth and tongue showing. You can burn incense in the fireplace and smoke will come out the chimney for a touch of authenticity.

The logs are authentic, too. She uses tiny twigs and branches and cuts them to size. A few extra sit on the hearth.

Laura had been hankering to do something like this all her life. She combined her love of painting, crafts, dolls and the Ozarks—where she was born, reared and plans to remain—and put them all together in this delightful look-back at part of America's heritage—the log cabin.

Laura Lee Hicken, folk artist

Laura's Cabin

This pioneer cabin is made from native Ozark wood, with cedar logs, shaker shingles, and incense-burning fireplace. House has a loft, downstairs, and front porch with swing and skunk-hide on the wall. Included are 51 porcelain and wood accessories, all handmade and handpainted. A family of 4 porcelain dolls (1" to 1' scale), dressed pioneer style, includes mother (Laura), father, child, and baby. Special orders accepted for any style dress and nationality. Unassembled cabin, each doll, and miniatures all sold separately.

Price: $245 (assembled cabin, accessories, family)
      $110 (cabin only), $63 (family)
Size/Weight: 17" x 22½" x 15¼", 17 lbs.
         (cabin, accessories, family)

Laura Lee Hicken
Route 3, Box 208-A
Buffalo, MO 65622
(417) 345-6332

Brochure available.
Commissions accepted.

Folk Scherenschnittes
Made of 100% rag paper scissor cut into a variety of designs. Each mounted on colored matboard with frame and glass. Choose floral wreath (5" x 5"), Christmas angel (5" x 7"), bears (5" x 4"), pineapple (4" x 5"), apple (5" x 5"), and light green, dark green, blue, or red mat.

Price/Size: $14.50 (4" x 5", 5" x 5"), $16.50 (5" x 7")
Weight: 9 oz.

Thom Rakes
Denise Matroni
Hearthstone
4360 Bainbridge Court
Columbia, MO 65203
(314) 445-2518

Commissions accepted.

Loving Wall Hanging
A stacked, three-dimensional goose, heart, and square, handcut of white pine. Sealed, handsanded, and painted in bright acrylic colors.

Price: $12
Size: 4¾" x 4¾" x 1"
Weight: 4 oz.

Marie E. Kelly
Country Crafts
P.O. Box 10345
Springfield, MO 65808
(417) 865-1510

Brochure forthcoming.
Commissions accepted.

Clown with Balloons
Bread dough ornament with polka-dot suit and colorful balloons.

Price: $5
Size: 4" x 1¾" x ¾"
Weight: 3 oz.

Missouri Fisherman
With green hip boots, red plaid shirt, fishing hat with lures, pole, and the "big catch."

Price: $5
Size: 4" x 1¾" x ¾"
Weight: 3 oz.

Gary and Michele Lindsey
1368 Trails Dr.
Fenton, MO 63026
(314) 677-8829

Brochure available.

Ol' Kris Kringle
This white pine Santa from Noel is painted with acrylic colors and finished with polyurethane for indoor and outdoor use.

Price: $29.49
Size: 19" x 12" x ¾"
Weight: 2½ lbs.

Mary Tarwater
P.O. Box 306
Route 1, Hwy. 59 North
Noel, MO 64854
(417) 475-3624
(417) 475-3636

Mary Mutton
Sheep made of cotton fleece fabric over 2″ wooden base. Face and legs handpainted. Not a toy. Available in black or white.

Price: $27
Size: 15″ x 7½″ x 20″
Weight: 2 lbs.

Lana Kramer
LK Ltd.
5541 S. Hazel
Springfield, MO 65807
(417) 887-6852

Commissions accepted.

Prairie Friends
Wide-eyed little dolls cut from Missouri maple, then individually painted in country colors and attire. Each piece is aged and "antiqued," then finished with a matte finish.

Price: $6.50
Size: 3″ x 2½″ x ½″
Weight: 3 oz.

Susie Wimmer
803 N. Walker
Montgomery City, MO 63361
(314) 564-3532

Brochure available.

Real Flower Cards
Made by pressing garden and/or wildflowers of northern Missouri, mounting on cards, and covering with clear, self-adhesive cover. "Thinking of you" imprinted on some.

Price: $6.95 (for 3)
Size: 6" x 4½"

Hazel M. Putnam
Box 226
Unionville, MO 63565
(816) 947-2766
(816) 947-2043

Miniature Fruit and Vegetable Baskets
These bread dough miniatures are individually handcrafted, air-dried, and dipped several times in urethane. Suitable for display in miniature boxes or doll house.

Price: $2.95
Size: cornucopia (2 cm. x 3 cm. x 4.5 cm.),
       vegetable/fruit
       baskets (3 cm. x 3 cm. x 2 cm.)

Ellen Tucker
505 North St.
East Prairie, MO 63845
(314) 649-2894

Braided Wool Rugs
Handbraided, heavy, long-lasting rugs laced with linen thread.
Various colors and sizes available. Dry clean only.

Price/Size: $60 (2' x 3' "hit and miss") to $300 (3' x 5')

Rachel Whitesitt
Box 167
Salisbury, MO 65281
(816) 388-5977

Commissions only.

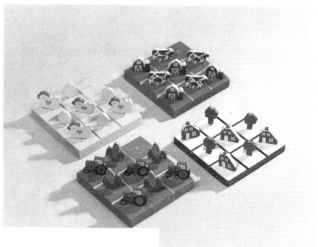

Tic-Tac-Toe Games
These games are made of quality wood that is handpainted and finished. Available in over 18 designs and a variety of colors. Games pictured are: geese, dolls, angels, bears, hearts, chicken and eggs, barn and cow, tractor and corn, house and tree, Amish sitting, Amish standing, and Amish and buggy.

Price: $15
Size: 2" x 5" x 5"
Weight: 6 oz.

Randy and Debby Brunken
Country Companions
P.O. Box 382
Moberly, MO 65270
(816) 263-0717

Commissions accepted.

Country Checkers

These game boards come complete with wooden checkers.
Available in today's "country" colors. Styles include Amish
lady or Aunt Jemima (12" x 7½"), heart (20" x 20"), and square
(12" x 12"). Other game boards available.

Price: $65 (heart), $35 (square), $30 (Amish), $30 (Aunt Jemima)

Ann Caryl Worland
309 West Page
Vandalia, MO 63382
(314) 594-6250

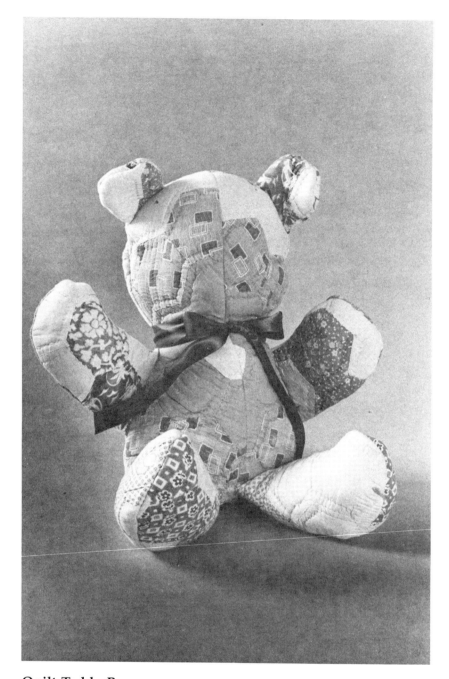

Quilt Teddy Bear
Made of old quilts and stuffed with polyfill. All washable.

Price: $20
Size: 18″ x 13″
Weight: 1 lb.

Evelyn M. LaChance
Box 5
Caledonia, MO 63631
(314) 779-3478

Commissions accepted.

Corn Husk Dolls

Available styles are egg lady (brown and tangerine), candle maker (Williamsburg blue and pink), southern lady (blue, pink and red), wash lady (pink or blue), sweeper (blue), cleaner lady (brown and rose), and angel (natural).

Price: $25
Size: 7-7½" tall

Corn Husk Angels

All in natural color with corn silk hair.

Price: $17
Size: 6" tall

Maple Flowers

Handwhittled flowers of soft maple. All in one piece, with wood twigs for stems. May be left natural color or spraypainted. Do not dip in water.

Price/Size: $1.75 (2½-3" across)
$1.25 (1½-2"), $1
(1")

Wilma M. Neal
Route 1, Box 183
Stewartsville, MO 64490
(816) 669-3328

Spicy Potpourri Heart
Soft, old-fashioned look,
handcrafted with dried
flowers, cinnamon sticks, and
bay nestled in baby's breath.
Choose satin ribbon of blue,
pink, or mauve.

Price: $27.50
Size: 10½" x 10½" x 3"
Weight: 1 lb. (approx.)

Herbal Wreath

This aromatic door wreath is made from home-grown herbs and flowers, including marjoram, sweet basil, lavender, bay, sage, cinnamon, yarrow, and dried flowers.

Price: $32.50
Size: 12" x 4"
Weight: 1 lb.

Heart's Desire

Delicate heart wreath includes baby's breath, yarrow, and star flowers. Flowers and ribbon in your choice of rose pink, blue, or mauve, all on ivory background.

Price: $22.50
Size: 8½" x 8½" x 2½"
Weight: 12 oz.

Carol Wilson
Gatherings
800 S. First
Odessa, MO 64076
(816) 633-7305

Brochure available ($1).
Commissions accepted.

The Renaissance Angel Series
This handpainted ornament is an exact reproduction of the designer's original handcarved ornament. Each ornament is cast in a plastic resin then finished to appear to be made of wood. There are 14 different designs, dating from 1981.

Price: $18
Size: 3½" x 2" x 4"
Weight: 1½-2 oz.

Kathy Killip
Underbrush, Ltd.
5100 Lee's Summit Rd.
Kansas City, MO 64136
(816) 373-4135

Commissions accepted.

Chinese Art
Goose egg.
Price: $25
Size: 5½ x 2½
Weight: 1 oz.

Farm Scene
Goose egg.
Price: $25
Size: 5½" x 2½"
Weight: 1 oz.

Ship and Whale
Ostrich egg from Africa.
Price: $95
Size: 10" x 5"
Weight: 8 oz.

These eggs are blown, then dyed with onion skins. Designs are scratched on with a knife, the eggs are glued to white walnut bases, and covered with plastic polymer. The goose eggs and wood are from Cabool, Missouri. All are signed. Other styles and eggs are available.

Evelyn Vandivort
Route 3, Box 528
Pacific, MO 63069
(314) 257-3339

Commissions accepted.

These animals are made from Rex rabbit fur, which does not shed, and have real leather parts and fiberfill stuffing. Furrier clean only. Both animals shown can be used as pajama bags and are available in a variety of colors, solid and spotted.

Standing Bunny Rabbit
Tricolor real fur bunny with childproof eyes.

Price: $85
Size: 13″ tall
Weight: 2 lbs.

Teddy Bear
Bear has leather paws and ears, childproof eyes and nose and comes in three different patterns.

Price: $100
Size: 14″ tall
Weight: 2 lbs.

Kenneth Cook
Mr. Kens Furs
R.R. 3, Box 231
California, MO 65018
(816) 458-6596

Commissions accepted.

Tree Top Angel
Hollow angel will fit over the top of your tree. Handpainted in antique red and ivory, with gold halo and accents. Lace ruffle and ribbon bow included.

Price: $37
Size: 10½" x 7" x 3½"
Weight: 8 oz.

Noel Wreath
White pine wreath painted in ivory and forest green with attached red bow, holly, and berries. Weatherproof finish.

Price: $68·
Size: 19¾" diameter
Weight: 3 lbs., 3 oz.

Jane Meyer
Route 7
2313 Lakewood Rd.
Jefferson City, MO 65101
(314) 636-4862

Commissions accepted.

Grandma and the Wolf Rod Puppets
The heads and shoulders are made from papier-mache, the arms are sewn fabric stuffed with sawdust. A rod is inserted into the unit to support it. All fabrics handsewn. Other puppets available.

Price: $400
Size: 22" x 8" x 5-10"
Weight: 4 lbs.

Jennifer Watt
Route 2, Box 415A
Villa Ridge, MO 63089
(314) 742-5483

Commissions accepted.

Butterfly
Swivel hook and nylon cord included. Choose red/yellow, turquoise/gold, or lilac/goldenrod. Dowel stick not included.

Price: $15
Size: 28″ x 26″ x ¼″
Weight: 8 oz.

These colorful nylon banners can be hung from porch post, tree bough, or any place they can catch the wind.

Bird
Blue and gold, with every edge of the nylon heat-sealed. Dowel stick not included.

Price: $15
Size: 28″ x 26″ x ¼″
Weight: 8 oz.

Flying Fish
Price: $17
Size: 40″ x 20″ x ¼″
Weight: 9 oz.

Ginger Baile and Myrna Ragar
Ragar-Baile
202 E. 4th St.
Sedalia, MO 65301
(816) 826-9357

Brochure available.
Commissions accepted.

Lillianna
This fully-jointed teddy made of 1″ bone-colored acrylic fur has a humped back, hand-embroidered nose and mouth, and velveteen pads. An original design. Other bears available from $35 to $80. Send $3 and self-addressed stamped envelope for sample packet ($3 refundable with first order).

Lillian Hahn
The Bear House
626 E. Main
Jackson, MO 63755
(314) 243-3743

Brochure and sample packet available.
Commissions accepted.

Farm Wagon Riding and Pull Toy

This replica of an old farm wagon has an oak steering mechanism, poplar handle and undercarriage, and pine box and seat. Axles are ½" and secured to undercarriage by eyebolts. Lawnmower wheels (7" and 8") with red enamel undercarriage and handle and black metal parts. Specify red or green for box. Easy to pull. Shipped by bus or freight.

Price: $195.00
Size: 21" x 24" x 36"

Staked Wagon Pull Toy

A little red wagon with removable white stakes is easy to pull and steer. Box, stakes, and undercarriage made of pine. Plastic 6" wheels secured to frame with ½" x 3½" bolts. Black, white, and red lead-free enamel colors.

Price: $48
Size: 13" x 15" x 20"

June and Bob Landgraf
Jun-Bob Crafts
Route 1, Box 177
Jackson, MO 63755
(314) 243-5912

Mouth Puppets

Full-body puppet, with moveable mouth and one or both hands controlled by rods. Available half-body.

Price: $60 (and up)
Size: 30″ tall (approx.)
Weight: 2-4 lbs.

Each puppet style shown comes in a variety of characters.

Animal and Fantasy Puppets

These puppets include the Great Eagle; Douglas D. Dragon, an all-wood, rocking control marionette, perfect for beginners; and the "huggables," designed to entertain young children.

Price: $17-$85
Size: 9-32" tall
Weight: 1-4 lbs.

Finger Puppets

These puppets are operated with three fingers.

Price: $4.50-$13

Andrea and Gerry Sparks

Mastercraft Puppets
P.O. Box 39
Branson, MO 65616
(417) 546-4287

Commissions accepted.

The Missouri Wreath
Made from dried plants and grasses, nuts, lichen, and cones,
all native to the fields and hills of Arcadia Valley, Missouri. It
includes veined and colorful rocks from the state (some of the
earliest evidences of traceable rock formation in North
America). No two alike. A descriptive card accompanies each.

Price: $18
Size: 9″ diameter x 3″
Weight: 8 oz.

Mary Lou Klassen
Route 1, Box 123A
Arcadia, MO 63621

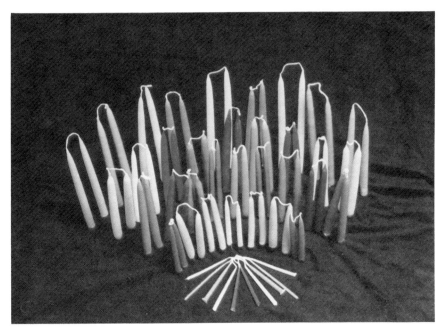

Hand-Dipped Candles

Candles are made from handforged equipment and have a high melting point, slow-burning wax, and braided wick. Softly scented. Come in 15 colors and 6 sizes. Minimum order: $2.25.

Price: $.33 (per pair, minis) to $2.09 (per pair, 10″) (includes shipping)

Ami Leighter
Route 2, Box 192
Grain Valley, MO 64029
(816) 228-5090
(816) 221-4642

Brochure available.
Commissions accepted.

Candles available in autumn yellow, colonial blue, hunter green, country red, brown, and bittersweet.

Corn Candle

Made from fully refined scented wax in approximately 14 steps. It will withstand high temperature. The original model was an ear of Missouri-grown Indian corn. Shuck not included.

Price: $6 ($14 for 3)
Size: 7″ long, 1½″ diameter
Weight: 5 oz.

Corn Candle Arrangement

Consists of scented corn candle, stained and varnished 4″ x 4″ wooden stand, and woven loop of wheat with decorative bow.

Price: $11.50
Size: 8½″ x 4″ x 4″
Weight: 11 oz.

Harriet Platz
Candles by Hawkins
P.O. Box 346
Shelbina, MO 63468
(314) 588-4731
(314) 588-4008

White Chocolate After Dinner Mints
Available September 1-April 31. Comes in red box with gold bow.

Price: $5.95
Weight: 6 oz.

Luxury Chocolate Assortment
Available November 1-March 31. Assortment of milk and dark chocolates gift-wrapped in gold foil with a bow.

Price: $14.95 (1 lb.), $8.49 (½ lb.)

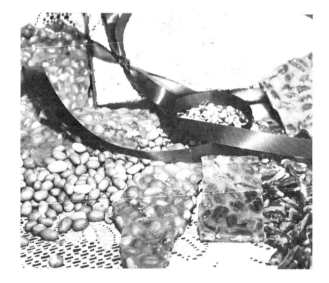

Gourmet Nut Brittle
Available all year.

Price (per pound): $7.95 (peanuts), $8.95 (pecans)
$9.95 (Missouri black walnuts)

Handmade candy with no preservatives.

Neika Z. Soisson
Route 4, Box 40
Sullivan, MO 63080
(314) 468-4504

Brochure available.
Commissions accepted.

indexes

Information about 2nd edition of
Best of Missouri's Hands

Missouri residents only, if you would like to be considered for the next edition of the Best of Missouri's Hands, please send a self-addressed stamped envelope to:

Best of Missouri's Hands
628 Clark Hall
University of Missouri
Columbia, Missouri 65211

Please send me ____ copies of the *Best of Missouri's Hands* catalogue at $14.95 each, including shipping and handling, (Missouri residents add $.97 sales tax). Make check payable to "University of Missouri."

Enclosed is my check for _____ .

Please ship to:

Name _____

Address _____

City _____ State ____ Zip _____

Please check here if you wish to be notified of future editions of this catalogue: _____

Best of Missouri's Hands
628 Clark Hall
Drawer 2
University of Missouri
Columbia, Missouri 65211

Please send me ____ copies of the *Best of Missouri's Hands* catalogue at $14.95 each, including shipping and handling, (Missouri residents add $.97 sales tax). Make check payable to "University of Missouri."

Enclosed is my check for _____ .

Please ship to:

Name _____

Address _____

City _____ State ____ Zip _____

Please check here if you wish to be notified of future editions of this catalogue: _____

Best of Missouri's Hands
628 Clark Hall
Drawer 2
University of Missouri
Columbia, Missouri 65211

Please send me copies of the *Best of Missouri's Hands* catalogue at $14.95 each, including shipping and handling, (Missouri residents add $.97 sales tax). Make check payable to "University of Missouri."

Enclosed is my check for _____ .

Please ship to:

Name _____

Address _____

City _____ State ___ Zip _____

Please check here if you wish to be notified of future editions of this catalogue: _____

Best of Missouri's Hands
628 Clark Hall
Drawer 2
University of Missouri
Columbia, Missouri 65211

Please send me copies of the *Best of Missouri's Hands* catalogue at $14.95 each, including shipping and handling, (Missouri residents add $.97 sales tax). Make check payable to "University of Missouri."

Enclosed is my check for _____ .

Please ship to:

Name _____

Address _____

City _____ State ___ Zip _____

Please check here if you wish to be notified of future editions of this catalogue: _____

Best of Missouri's Hands
628 Clark Hall
Drawer 2
University of Missouri
Columbia, Missouri 65211